Contents

MERSEA ISLAND SCHOOL
BARFIELD ROAD
WEST MERSEA
ESSEX CO5 8QX
Tel: 01206 382736

What characteristics might gifted mathematicians display?

More able mathematicians are likely to have good powers of logic, reasoning and deduction, and will be able to hypothesise, experiment and categorise. This list of questions may be useful in establishing mathematical ability:

- Do they enjoy number puzzles?
- Do they show a good awareness of patterns and sequences?
- Do they ask interesting mathematical questions?
- Do they give explanations you may not have thought of?
- Are they good at solving problems?
- Are they good at applying knowledge in unfamiliar contexts?
- Do they like to choose their own methods?

This list is by no means exhaustive; there are many more characteristics that may be observed in gifted mathematicians, and many gifted children will display only some of these qualities. For example, a child who you believe to be a high achiever may not show advanced problem-solving skills. This may be because they don't yet know how to set about solving a problem, because they haven't learned the strategies required. You may find children who are gifted in just one or two areas of maths. For example, they may excel at calculation and number, but may not do so well at shape and space.

What about children who don't show any of these traits?

There may be gifted mathematicians in your class who do not display any of these characteristics. This could be due to one or more of these factors:

- lack of confidence
- unwillingness to stand out from their peers
- the desire to avoid 'extra' work
- an insufficiently stimulating learning environment
- lack of challenging activities
- lack of familiarity with basic number facts and skills
- language barriers
- problems with reading and/or writing.

What can be done to identify gifted mathematicians?

Here are a few suggestions of practical steps that can be taken:

- Ask parents and carers to supply information about any mathematical abilities they have noticed at home.
- Conduct a brief interview with children at the beginning of the school year to find out about their interests and anything they think they are especially good at.
- Keep a portfolio of particularly good work completed either at home or in school. This will help to assess progress and spot patterns.
- Testing can provide evidence of high ability, but you should be aware that some more able or gifted children may not perform well in tests, and many factors can affect children's performance in a test environment.

The identification–provision cycle

A two-way process of identification and provision is needed. You will not be able to observe exceptional abilities in children unless they are given the opportunity to demonstrate them. Activities must be provided that challenge children and allow them the scope to show what they can do. In this way, appropriate provision leads to identification, which in turn allows you to make better provision.

How can a stimulating learning environment be created?

It is important that more able children are asked probing and open-ended questions. These will allow you to assess and extend their understanding, get them to think more deeply, and lead them to continue their explorations. Here are some examples of the types of question you might ask:

- What do you think will happen if …?
- How many different ways can you …?
- Is it always true that …?
- Why?
- What patterns can you see?
- Why did you choose to work it out like that?
- Why do you think this happens?
- How do you know that?
- Can you make up a rule?

It is also important to create an atmosphere in which children feel they are able to ask questions, and have access to resources to find the answers. One practical thing you can do is to create a 'Challenge corner': an area of the classroom where you can set out maths resources, puzzles, prompts and questions for children to explore. This should be accessible by all children in the class, giving everyone the opportunity to challenge themselves.

What are 'challenge' activities?

'Challenging' work can be defined as something difficult that requires the learner to learn something new. For children to enjoy a challenging activity there must be something about it that motivates them. For example, it could be about a subject that they are particularly interested in, or it could be placed in a meaningful context, with a goal that has nothing to do with completing a page of calculations. The level of challenge must be just right – it must stretch them without being so difficult that children are demotivated and want to give up. The best challenge activities will allow different levels of outcome, so that a wide range of children can succeed at them.

More able or gifted children need to be given opportunities to:

- exercise their curiosity and explore new ideas
- choose their own ways of working and representing their results
- ask questions and find the answers
- make conjectures and test them out
- discuss their ideas with adults and other children
- reflect on their own work.

What thinking skills should more able children be using?

More able children need to be given opportunities to access their higher-order thinking skills. Bloom's Taxonomy identifies six levels of thinking:

- knowledge – the acquisition and recall of facts
- comprehension – the ability to describe what you know in your own words
- application – the application of what you have learned in context
- analysis – for example, categorising things and identifying patterns
- synthesis – the creation of new ideas or products
- evaluation – the evaluation of ideas, processes and products.

The first three are generally thought of as lower-order skills, although application requires a deeper level of thinking than the first two. If you can plan activities that incorporate the three higher-order thinking skills, children will be challenged.

What is *Abacus Evolve Challenge*?

Abacus Evolve Challenge is designed to stretch and motivate more able mathematicians. The activities are creative and engaging, and offer opportunities for written, verbal and practical work. Using and applying skills are practised throughout, with plenty of open-ended investigations and problem solving. Speaking and listening skills are promoted through the high proportion of paired and group work.

Which children is *Challenge* for?

Challenge is not just for those children who would be classed as 'gifted'. The activities have been written with the whole of the 'top table' in mind. Differentiation by outcome is often possible because of the open-ended nature of the activities, and the teacher notes accompanying the activities usually suggest ways to differentiate further.

What types of enrichment and extension are provided?

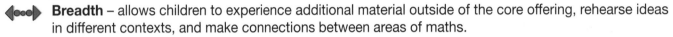 **Breadth** – allows children to experience additional material outside of the core offering, rehearse ideas in different contexts, and make connections between areas of maths.

Depth – is achieved by asking children to delve deeper into the concepts. It is about thinking intellectually.

 **Pace** – refers to speed in covering the curriculum and can result in achievement at a level exceptional for the age range.

What types of activity are provided?

Adult-led – these activities allow children to work with an adult. There are two adult-led activities per two-week block.

Practise – these activities allow children to practise what they have learned with the rest of the class, at a higher level.

Discover – these activities allow children to learn about things like famous mathematicians and ancient number systems.

Investigate – these activities allow children to explore a concept freely, asking questions, looking for patterns and drawing conclusions.

When should the *Challenge* activities be used?

There are 90 activities per Year; six for every two-week block. They are intended to be used by small groups of children in the part of the maths lesson when the class is split into groups for differentiated work. This allows the more able children to be included in the whole-class parts of the lesson.

What level of adult support is needed?

The *Challenge* resources have been designed with effective classroom management in mind. Four of the activities in each two-week block can be carried out by children without adult support, allowing you to focus on the other groups. Some of these will require a couple of minutes to get the group started on the activity, but after this children should be able to continue unaided.

Two of the activities in each two-week block require adult support, so that your able and gifted children have the benefits of adult input.

How does *Challenge* fit alongside the *Abacus Evolve* maths scheme?

The *Challenge* activities are organised using the same blocked structure as *Abacus Evolve*. You can use the *Abacus Evolve* weekly plans, and fit the *Challenge* activities into these. *Abacus Evolve* objectives are referenced for each activity, and these will help you to decide which core activities to run them alongside. If you also have the *Challenge* module of I-Planner Online, you will be able to see the *Challenge* activities allocated to suitable days in the weekly plans.

It is intended that the more able children join in with the whole-class parts of the lesson: the mental oral starter, the main teaching activity, and the plenary. When the rest of the class is split up into 1-dot, 2-dot and 3-dot groups to do Textbook activities or practical activities, you can give your top group a *Challenge* activity that fits in well with what the rest of the class are doing.

Can I use *Challenge* with another maths scheme or my own planning?

Although the *Challenge* activities complement *Abacus Evolve* activities, they are not specifically linked to them, so there is no dependence on any part of the *Abacus Evolve* scheme. The *Challenge* activities can be used to accompany any other maths scheme or your own planning. You can search for *Challenge* activities that fit your teaching by looking at the Renewed Framework objectives in the Teacher Guide. All of the Renewed Framework objectives are covered by the *Challenge* activities.

What resources are in the *Challenge* range?

Each Year includes:

- a Teacher Guide
- a Textbook
- an I-Planner Online Module.

Teacher Guide

The Teacher Guide contains detailed notes to accompany each activity. The information provided includes:

- Suggested group size and adult support
- Resources required (Textbook pages, Photocopy Masters and other resources)
- *Abacus Evolve* objectives
- Renewed Framework objectives
- A description of the activity
- 'Extra help': ideas for differentiating at a lower level
- 'Further extension': ideas for differentiating at a higher level
- 'If you have time': ideas for continuing the activity
- Background maths information for the non-specialist teacher
- 'Be aware': things to watch out for, such as common misconceptions
- Outcomes for the activity, given in child-friendly language
- Ideas for other resources to support the activity, such as useful websites.

Textbook

There are five Textbook pages per two-week block, so nearly every activity has an accompanying Textbook page. The pages are colourful and engaging, and they include the following features:

- speech bubbles to indicate opportunities for discussion
- an Extra activity at the bottom of each page for children who finish early.

The Textbook pages are not just intended for children to use individually. They are often suitable for paired or group work.

I-Planner Online

The *Abacus Evolve* I-Planner is a powerful online tool that provides ready-to-use weekly, medium-term and yearly plans that are completely flexible. It can save hours of planning time, but allows you to adapt the plans to meet the exact needs of your class. The *Challenge* module of I-Planner for each Year includes an extra column in the weekly plans in which you can see all the *Challenge* activities allocated to suitable days. This allows you to plan the *Challenge* activities seamlessly into your maths lessons.

What support is provided for assessing the children?

The adult-led activities are ideal for day-to-day observational assessment, as they provide plenty of opportunities to work closely with the children and ask probing questions to ascertain their level of understanding.

The charts on pages 8–11 of this book show the Assessment Foci from the Assessing Pupils' Progress guidelines, and the *Challenge* activities that can be used to provide evidence towards this type of assessment.

On pages 106–115 of this book you will find three end-of-term investigative activities. These will allow you to assess how well children use and apply the skills they have built up over the term.

Icon guide

Group size

 Children working individually, without an adult

 Children working in pairs, without an adult

 Children working in groups, without an adult

 Children working in groups, with an adult

Type of resource

 Textbook

 Photocopy Master

 Additional resources

Type of enrichment/extension

 Breadth

 Depth

 Pace

Type of activity

 Adult-led

 Practise

 Discover

 Investigate

Support for Assessing Pupils' Progress

If you are using Assessing Pupils' Progress to assess children, you may find this chart helpful when deciding which of the *Challenge* activities could be used to provide evidence towards each Assessment Focus.

We do not recommend that you use every activity to make an assessment. It is also important to recognise that a full assessment cannot be made on the basis of the *Challenge* activities alone; you will need to draw on other sources of information as well. We would advise that in each block of work you use this chart as guidance towards choosing one activity to assess against APP criteria, to complement other day-to-day or periodic assessments.

Most of the Year 4 *Challenge* activities should give children the opportunity to work at a secure Level 4.

Ma1 Using and applying mathematics

	Problem solving	Communicating	Reasoning
Level 4	• A1.3 Find the number • C1.2 Pairs of tetrominoes • C1.4 Showing data in different ways • A2.2 Adding sequences with Gauss • A2.4 Six circles • A2.4 Exploring arithmagons • B2.6 Pentominoes and cube nets • C2.1 Capacity puzzles • D2.2 Palindromes • D2.6 High score squares • E2.4 Sharing camels • B3.4 Bearings • C3.1 Roads between towns • C3.4 Half times • E3.4 Fractions of a square	• A1.3 Find the number • B1.6 2D shape patterns • C1.5 All sorts of bears • E1.1 Patterns in multiples • C2.6 Graphs and the data handling cycle • B3.2 Multiplying and dividing by 9 • B3.5 Hexominoes • C3.5 Carroll and Venn diagrams • C3.6 Putting data into logic diagrams • D3.5 Investigating patterns from 7s • E3.2 Multiplication patterns	• A1.6 Packing boxes • B1.4 Investigating 2D shapes • C1.3 Areas of rectangles • D1.2 Adding consecutive numbers • E1.1 Patterns in multiples • A2.2 Adding sequences with Gauss • A2.3 Estimating game • A2.4 Six circles • A2.5 Exploring arithmagons • B2.3 Steps to triangular numbers • B2.5 Properties of polyhedra • C2.1 Capacity puzzles • D2.1 Number target • D2.2 Palindromes • E2.3 Into the unknown • A3.4 Subtraction walls • A3.6 Patterns in subtractions • B3.1 Kaprekar's numbers • B3.3 Digital roots • C3.1 Roads between towns • D3.1 Back numbers • D3.5 Investigating patterns from 7s • D3.6 Multiplying odd and even numbers

Ma2 Number

	Numbers and the number system	Fractions, decimals, percentages and ratio	Operations, relationships between them
Level 4	• A1.1 Double or quits • A2.1 Larger numbers • A2.6 Positive and negative number loops • B2.3 Steps to triangular numbers • A3.3 The Gattegno chart • E3.1 Factor record-breakers	• E1.5 Fraction games • E1.6 Investigating fraction sentences • E2.5 Fractions in order • E2.6 Tenths link cards • D3.3 Half-price sale • E3.5 Fractions and decimals link cards • E3.6 Missing fractions and decimals	• A1.5 Splitting one hundred • A1.6 Packing boxes • D2.1 Number target • D2.4 Missing-number subtractions • B3.2 Multiplying and dividing by 9
Level 3		• D1.5 Fractions of 60 • E2.4 Sharing camels	• D1.3 Adding and subtracting near decades

Ma2 Number

	Mental methods	Solving numerical problems	Written and calculator methods
Level 4	• A1.1 Double or quits • A1.4 Triple multiplying • A1.5 Splitting one hundred • B1.1 Extending number pairs • B1.3 Number pair card game • D1.1 Hexadria • E1.4 Doubling and halving with fractions • A2.1 Larger numbers • B2.2 Doubling chains • D2.4 Missing-number subtractions • E2.1 Multiplying by doubling and halving • E2.3 Into the unknown • A3.4 Subtraction walls • A3.5 Matching subtractions • D3.2 Subtraction options • D3.6 Multiplying odd and even numbers • E3.1 Factor record-breakers	• B1.2 Word problems • A2.3 Estimating game • D2.3 Subtraction matching game • D2.5 The bill • A3.1 Rounding link cards • A3.2 Estimating perimeters and areas • C3.2 Maps • C3.3 Mass and weight • D3.1 Back numbers • D3.3 Half-price sale	• D2.3 Subtraction matching game • D2.5 The bill • D2.6 High score squares • A3.6 Patterns in subtractions • B3.1 Kaprekar's numbers • B3.3 Digital roots • D3.2 Subtraction options • E3.2 Multiplication patterns
Level 3	• D1.3 Adding and subtracting near decades • E1.2 Sum, difference and product • E1.3 Rainbow patterns • E2.2 Maximising products		• E1.2 Sum, difference and product • E2.2 Maximising products

Ma3 Shape, space and measures

	Properties of shape	Properties of position and movement	Measures
Level 4	• B1.4 Investigating 2D shapes • B1.6 2D shape patterns • B2.1 Halving and doubling shapes • B2.4 Understanding tetrahedra • B2.5 Properties of polyhedra • B2.6 Pentominoes and cube nets • B3.5 Hexominoes • B3.6 Paper-folding angles	• B1.5 Rotational symmetry	• C1.2 Pairs of tetrominoes • D1.4 Before and after the hour • D1.6 Time zones • C2.3 Timetables • C2.4 Perimeter and area • C2.5 Side lengths and perimeters • C3.4 Half times
Level 3		• B3.4 Bearings • B3.5 Hexominoes	

Ma4 Handling data

	Processing and representing data	Interpreting data
Level 4	• C1.4 Showing data in different ways • C1.5 All sorts of bears • C2.6 Graphs and the data handling cycle • C3.5 Carroll and Venn diagrams • C3.6 Putting data into logic diagrams	• C1.4 Showing data in different ways • C1.6 Make your own pictograms
Level 3	• C1.6 Make your own pictograms	• C2.6 Graphs and the data handling cycle

Abacus Evolve *Talk Maths Extra* will reinforce key maths skills and get children talking about maths.

1 Place-value puzzle 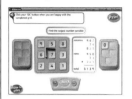	Create 2- and 3-digit numbers to make the largest and smallest totals possible.	**2 Shape detective** 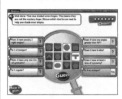	Find a mystery shape by eliminating shapes based on clues.
3 Pictograms and bar charts 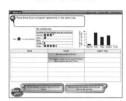	Decide whether statements about pictograms and bar charts are true or false.	**4 Number triangle** 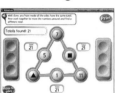	Place numbers so that each side has the same total.
5 Mystery number 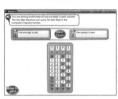	Find a mystery 4-digit number by eliminating digits based on clues.	**6 Always, sometimes, never** 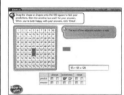	Investigate statements about sums of consecutive and adjacent numbers.
7 Half-a-shape 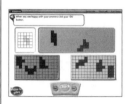	Work out what shapes could be made by fitting two identical shapes together.	**8 Add near multiples of 10** 	Make target numbers by adding near multiples of 10.
9 Function machine 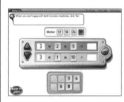	Make a product in two different ways by multiplying three numbers together.	**10 Ordering fractions** 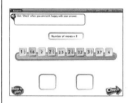	Place whole numbers, fractions and decimals in order.
11 Marble run 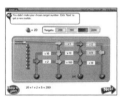	Make a number by selecting a path for a marble through various calculations.	**12 Trace-a-shape** 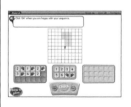	Describe a route to follow the outline of a shape.
13 Carroll diagram 	Place numbers onto a Carroll diagram, then choose labels to match.	**14 Domino products** 	Place dominoes so that touching ends multiply to give a product that fits the mystery rule.
15 Mystery decimal 	Find a mystery TU·th number by eliminating digits based on clues.	**16 Fraction flag** 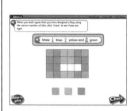	Design a flag using the specified fractions of blue, green and yellow tiles.
17 Units of measurement 	Select smaller units of length, capacity and weight to make up a larger unit.	**18 Measuring capacity** 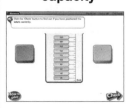	Complete the scale on a measuring beaker, then say how much water is in the beaker

This chart shows which *Talk Maths Extra* activities could be used to extend some of the *Challenge* activities. The 4-dot version of each *Talk Maths Extra* activity is likely to be the most suitable for your children.

Challenge activity	Related *Talk Maths Extra* activities
A1.1 Double or quits	5 Mystery number
A1.2 Roman numerals	1 Place-value puzzle
A1.3 Find the number	5 Mystery number
A1.4 Triple multiplying	9 Function machine
B1.4 Investigating 2D shape	2 Shape detective
B1.5 Rotational symmetry	7 Half-a-shape
C1.4 Showing data in different ways	3 Pictograms and bar charts
C1.6 Make your own pictograms	3 Pictograms and bar charts
D1.1 Hexadria	4 Number triangle
D1.2 Adding consecutive numbers	4 Number triangle, 6 Always, sometimes, never
D1.3 Adding and subtracting near decades	8 Add near multiples of 10
E1.1 Patterns in multiples	14 Domino products
E1.2 Sum, difference and product	6 Always, sometimes, never, 9 Function machine
E1.4 Doubling and halving with fractions	10 Ordering fractions, 16 Fraction flag
E1.5 Fraction games	16 Fraction flag
E1.6 Investigating fraction sentences	16 Fraction flag
A2.1 Larger numbers	1 Place-value puzzle
A2.2 Adding sequences with Gauss	6 Always, sometimes, never
A2.4 Six circles	8 Add near multiples of 10
A2.5 Exploring arithmagons	4 Number triangle
B2.1 Halving and doubling shapes	2 Shape detective
B2.2 Doubling chains	11 Marble run
C2.1 Capacity puzzles	17 Units of measurement, 18 Measuring capacity
C2.6 Graphs and the data handling cycle	3 Pictograms and bar charts
D2.2 Palindromes	1 Place-value puzzle
D2.3 Subtraction matching game	4 Number triangle
D2.5 The bill	15 Mystery decimals
E2.1 Multiplying by doubling and halving	9 Function machine
E2.4 Sharing camels	15 Mystery decimal
E2.5 Fractions in order	10 Ordering fractions, 15 Mystery decimal
E2.6 Tenths links cards	15 Mystery decimal
B3.5 Hexominoes	12 Trace-a-shape
C3.2 Maps	17 Units of measurement
C3.3 Mass and weight	17 Units of measurement
C3.5 Carroll and Venn diagrams	13 Carroll diagram
E3.4 Fractions of a square	16 Fraction flag
E3.5 Fractions and decimals link cards	16 Fraction flag
E3.6 Missing fractions and decimals	15 Mystery decimal

Abacus Evolve *Solve the Problem* will challenge children with rich, open-ended problems that draw on a range of mathematical strategies.

Pop tour

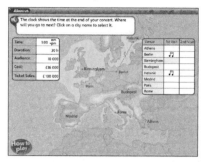

A pop band is touring Europe, trying to break the record for playing to the largest audience in the shortest time. There is also an added challenge of cost and profit. Children plan their route to eight European cities starting and ending at Birmingham.

Safari hospital

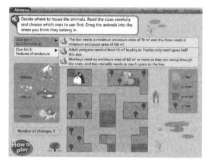

Children have ownership of a safari hospital and need to accommodate six types of animal. They must decide which of the enclosures suit which animal, paying attention to the area of the enclosure and the features within it.

Market day

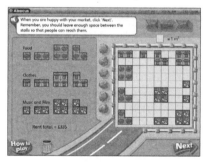

Children own a market with an area of 100 m². The aim is to create a market that is profitable by inviting different stall owners to set up and pay rent. However, the market must meet local council rules.

Football fans

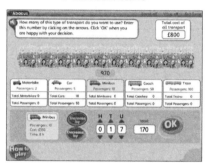

Children must transport 1020 fans to a football match in one or more of five ways: motorbike, car, minibus, coach or train. Children are given different challenges, for example transporting all the fans in the cheapest way possible.

Motor mania

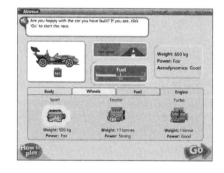

Children select features to build a vehicle to compete in four stages in a competition: flat sprint, off-road, push a tree and race track. The aim is to design a vehicle that will perform well in each stage of the race, achieving a good overall position.

Mini-golf

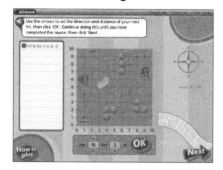

Children position holes on a map to create a mini-golf course. They plan a route to hit the ball into each hole, using direction and distance. The aim is to score maximum points without incurring penalty points for hitting obstacles.

This chart shows which *Solve the Problem* activities could be used to extend some of the *Challenge* activities. The *Solve the Problem* activities are suitable for all ability levels, as children can set their own problems.

Challenge activity	Related *Solve the Problem* activities
A1.3 Find the number	Motor mania
A1.6 Packing boxes	Football fans
C1.3 Areas of rectangles	Safari hospital
D1.4 Before and after the hour	Pop tour
D1.6 Time zones	Pop tour
E1.4 Doubling and halving with fractions	Market day
A2.3 Estimating game	Football fans
C2.3 Timetables	Pop tour
C2.3 Perimeter and area	Safari hospital
D2.1 Number target	Football fans
E2.2 Maximising targets	Market day
E2.3 Into the unknown	Football fans
B3.4 Bearings	Mini-golf
B3.5 Hexominoes	Mini-golf
C3.2 Maps	Mini-golf
C3.4 Half times	Mini-golf

Challenge Plan: Year 4

A1: whole numbers to 10 000; partitioning into Th, H, T and U; multiplication as repeated addition; dividing whole numbers

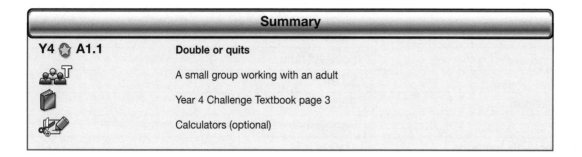

Summary

Y4 ⬡ A1.1

Double or quits

A small group working with an adult

Year 4 Challenge Textbook page 3

Calculators (optional)

Abacus Evolve objectives

- **Y5** Read and write whole numbers in figures and words, and know what each digit represents
- **Y5** Say one or more numbers lying between two given numbers (revise)
- **Y5** Double or halve 2-digit numbers by doubling or halving the tens first
- **Y5** Derive doubles of integers up to 100 and 2-digit decimals and their corresponding halves

Framework objectives

- **Y5** *Explain what each digit represents in whole numbers and decimals with up to two places, and partition, round and order these numbers*
- **Y5** *Use knowledge of place value and addition and subtraction of two-digit numbers to derive sums and differences and doubles and halves of decimals (e.g. 6·5 ± 2·7, half of 5·6, double 0·34)*

Teacher notes

Getting started
Introduce multiplying by 10, starting at 1 and getting to 10, 100, 1000. Draw from the group that the next number names are *ten thousand*, *one hundred thousand*, and *one million*.
Explain that the number 1 234 567 is read as *one million, two hundred and thirty-four thousand, five hundred and sixty-seven*.
Write 9 876 543 and ask children to write it in words.
Write this number in figures: eight hundred and twenty-one thousand, seven hundred and sixty-three.
If time allows, a minute or so of doubling practice could be useful before beginning the Textbook page.

Activity
Children work from Textbook page 3. They start from 1 and keep doubling, until they can go no further. Assist them in copying and completing the table. Suggest that they say some of the larger numbers out loud. If any struggle with doubling larger numbers, they may use a calculator to check.
Children then write out in words the numbers that appear in the doubling pattern between 1000 and 1 000 000.

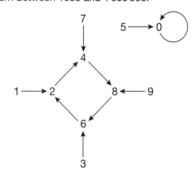

Information
1024 occurs with 10 doubles, and is nearly 1000. This gives a good approximation which is useful for the later effects of doubling. 20 doubles will be about 1 million, 30 doubles about 1 billion, and so on.

Be aware

- By now, children will be very proficient at doubling but this will test whether they have learnt methods they can use on any number. They may become surprised by the speed at which numbers grow when repeatedly doubled.

Outcomes

- I can read and write numbers up to a million in figures and words.
- I can recognise the value of each digit in any number up to a million.
- I can double large numbers up to a million.

Challenge Plan: Year 4

A1: whole numbers to 10 000; partitioning into Th, H, T and U; multiplication as repeated addition; dividing whole numbers

Summary

Y4 ⭐ A1.2

Roman numerals

Individuals, pairs or groups working independently

Year 4 Challenge Textbook page 4

Counters (optional); paper (optional)

Abacus Evolve objectives

- Read and write numbers up to 100 000 in figures and words
- Know what each digit in a 5-digit number represents
- Partition 4-digit numbers into Th, H, T and U
- Recognise the relationship between Th, H, T and U

Framework objectives

- Partition, round and order 4-digit whole numbers; use positive and negative numbers in context and position them on a number line; state inequalities using the symbols $<$ and $>$ (e.g. $^-3 > ^-5$, $^-1 < ^+1$)
- Identify and use patterns, relationships and properties of numbers or shapes; investigate a statement involving numbers and test it with examples

Teacher notes

Activity
Children work from Textbook page 4. They learn about the symbols used in Roman numerals and translate between numbers in Roman numerals and in our Arabic numerals. This activity is also useful for creating awareness of place value.

If you have time
Children can make Roman counting boards with lines drawn on paper, labelled, and with simple counters as calculi. They can use the boards to explore how addition and simple multiplication (by 2, 5, 10 or 100) is done.

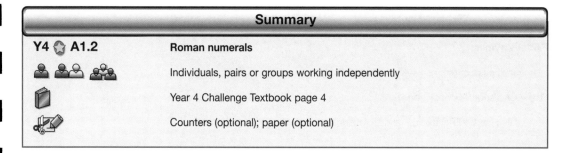

A Roman counting board,
showing MMIX or 2009

Information
No Roman counting boards have survived but they were widely used for many centuries throughout Europe.

Be aware

- As children are used to a place value numeral system, they may need time to appreciate the rules for composing numbers with letters.

Outcomes

- I can see how Roman numerals are used.
- I can change a number between Roman numerals and Arabic numerals.

Supporting resources

Children can find information on how Indian numerals formed the basis of the numbers we use in Europe today using:
- www-history.mcs.st-and.ac.uk/HistTopics/Arabic_numerals.html

For more information on the use of Roman numerals:
- http://www.yourdictionary.com/crossword/romanums.html

Challenge Plan: Year 4

A1: whole numbers to 10 000; partitioning into Th, H, T and U; multiplication as repeated addition; dividing whole numbers

Summary

Y4 ⬡ A1.3

Find the number

Individuals, pairs or groups working independently

Year 4 Challenge Textbook page 5

Place value cards (TTh, Th, H, T and U) (optional)

Abacus Evolve objectives	Framework objectives
• Partition 4-digit numbers into Th, H, T and U • Recognise the relationship between Th, H, T and U	• Partition, round and order 4-digit whole numbers; use positive and negative numbers in context and position them on a number line; state inequalities using the symbols < and > (e.g. $^-3 > {}^-5$, $^-1 < {}^+1$) • Solve one-step and two-step problems involving numbers, money or measures, including time; choose and carry out appropriate calculations, using calculator methods where appropriate • Suggest a line of enquiry and the strategy needed to follow it; collect, organise and interpret selected information to find answers

Teacher notes

Activity
Children work from Textbook page 5. They start off by matching statements to five 4-digit numbers. They then make up statements to match a second set of numbers. Lastly, they write their own set of numbers and make up statements to match. Children can then swap numbers and statements with other children in the group and solve each other's puzzles.

Extra help
If children need support, suggest they work together in pairs at the start.
Children could use place value cards to make their numbers, instead of writing them.

Further extension
When children write their own numbers, they could choose 5-digit or even 6-digit numbers.

If you have time
The group could work together to grade their sets of numbers and statements according to difficulty.
They could then produce a set of their puzzles to be 'published' within the school.

Be aware	Outcomes
• When making up clues children can draw on all knowledge and understanding to date. Make sure they are using this knowledge accurately.	• I can recognise whether or not numbers have certain properties. • I can use what I know about the properties of numbers to make up statements about them.

Challenge Plan: Year 4

A1: whole numbers to 10 000; partitioning into Th, H, T and U; multiplication as repeated addition; dividing whole numbers

Summary

Y4 ⬡ A1.4

Triple multiplying

Pairs or groups working independently

Year 4 Challenge Textbook page 6

Number cards 1–10; calculators (optional)

Abacus Evolve objectives

- Rehearse the concept of multiplication as describing an array
- Understand and use the commutativity of multiplication
- Consolidate division as the inverse of multiplication

Framework objectives

- *Derive and recall multiplication facts up to 10 × 10, the corresponding division facts and multiples of numbers to 10 up to the tenth multiple*
- Identify and use patterns, relationships and properties of numbers or shapes; investigate a statement involving numbers and test it with examples

Teacher notes

Preparation
Prepare a set of number cards 1–10, three sets per child. Also, preparing a simple sheet with three boxes in a line as on the Textbook page may help to keep children's recording neater.

Activity
Children work from Textbook page 6. They multiply sets of three digits and find the products.
Children then use number cards to make their own multiplications of three digits. They find the products and record these (they do not reveal the multipliers to other children). They then swap sheets and find the multipliers that would make each product.

Further extension
Using calculators, children can extend their range of multiplying up to 9 × 9 × 9 to produce further, more challenging puzzles. Others in the group use calculators to deduce the digits that have been multiplied.

If you have time
Discuss with the group the results of these multiplications:

2 × 5 × 6	2 × 6 × 5	5 × 2 × 6	5 × 6 × 2
6 × 2 × 5	6 × 5 × 2		

All the products are 60. Does this work for other sets of three numbers in different orders? Why is this?

Information
Children may recognise that any set of three digits will always give the same product. This may give insight into two laws of arithmetic:
The commutative law: $a \times b = b \times a$
The associative law: $a \times (b \times c) = (a \times b) \times c$.
Together these laws mean that any three numbers multiplied in any order give the same overall product.

Be aware

- Some children may be unused to multiplying three numbers together, and surprised by how large a product results.

Outcomes

- I can multiply three small numbers together.
- I can work out which three digits have been multiplied together to give a product.
- I can create puzzles for others to solve.

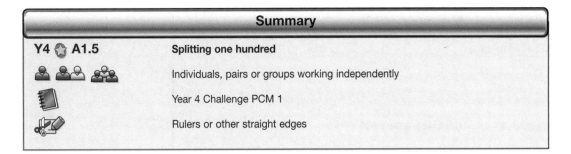

A1: whole numbers to 10 000; partitioning into Th, H, T and U; multiplication as repeated addition; dividing whole numbers

Summary

Y4 ★ A1.5

Splitting one hundred

Individuals, pairs or groups working independently

Year 4 Challenge PCM 1

Rulers or other straight edges

Abacus Evolve objectives

- **Y5** Know by heart all multiplication facts up to 10 × 10
- **Y5** Derive quickly division facts corresponding to multiplication facts up to 10 × 10

Framework objectives

- **Y5** Recall quickly multiplication facts up to 10 × 10 and use them to multiply pairs of multiples of 10 and 100; derive quickly corresponding division facts
- **Y5** Represent a puzzle or problem by identifying and recording the information or calculations needed to solve it; find possible solutions and confirm them in the context of the problem
- **Y5** Plan and pursue an enquiry; present evidence by collecting, organising and interpreting information; suggest extensions to the enquiry

Teacher notes

Preparation
Photocopy PCM 1, one or two copies per child.

Getting started
How many dots in the array? Children should recognise that it is 100, arrayed as 10 × 10 with gaps to show fives and twenty-fives. Also make sure that children can understand and use the words horizontal and vertical.

Activity
How many different ways of splitting 100 can you find?
- Ask children to draw one vertical line on the array. *How many dots are one side of the line? How many dots are on the other side of the line?* (Encourage children to use multiplying rather than counting.)
- Children repeat four times, then repeat with a horizontal line. They record these splits in the blank multiplication grids on PCM 1, like this. Children should be aware that they can write the multiplication either way round.
- Check that children understand by asking *How many dots in that group? How many in that group? How many altogether? How do you know? Use your multiplication grid to show me how you know.* Children should demonstrate that the total of the two multiplications is 100.

Vertical

×	7	3
10	70	30

Horizontal

×	10
8	80
2	20

Children then explore using both a vertical line and a horizontal line to split into four parts, for example the two lines in this array. They record these on the blank multiplication grids.
Children should begin to recognise the link between distributing and multiplying which helps when using the grid method of multiplication.

×	6	4
7	42	28
3	18	12

Further extension
Children can investigate splitting 200 dots (two 100 arrays next to each other), then 400 dots (four 100 arrays in a square). Results should be recorded in multiplication grids as before.

Information
These arrays show children how the grid method of multiplication works.

Be aware

- Some children may not initially be aware that the split parts still add up to the original amount.

Outcomes

- I can split multiplications and record them on a grid.
- I understand that the total stays the same when a multiplication is split.

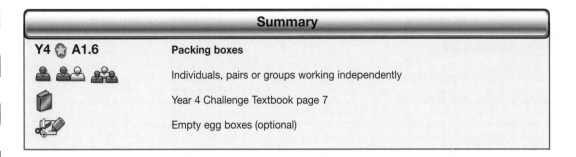

Challenge Plan: Year 4

A1: whole numbers to 10 000; partitioning into Th, H, T and U; multiplication as repeated addition; dividing whole numbers

Summary

Y4 ⭐ A1.6

Packing boxes

Individuals, pairs or groups working independently

Year 4 Challenge Textbook page 7

Empty egg boxes (optional)

Abacus Evolve objectives

- Consolidate division as the inverse of multiplication
- Rehearse the concept of division as grouping
- Find remainders after division
- Continue to round up or down after division, depending on the context
- Know the multiplication facts for the 6 times table, and the corresponding division facts
- Begin to know the multiplication facts for the 8 times table, and the corresponding division facts

Framework objectives

- *Develop and use written methods to record, support and explain multiplication and division of two-digit numbers by a one-digit number, including division with remainders (e.g. 15 × 9, 98 ÷ 6)*
- *Derive and recall multiplication facts up to 10 × 10, the corresponding division facts and multiples of numbers to 10 up to the tenth multiple*
- Solve one-step and two-step problems involving numbers, money or measures, including time; choose and carry out appropriate calculations, using calculator methods where appropriate

Teacher notes

Getting started
If you have brought in some egg boxes, give them to the children to look at. This will help to link the activity to the real-life context.

Activity
Children work from Textbook page 7. They solve problems involving packing food items into boxes of different sizes. Children are encouraged to explore different numbers to be packed and look for patterns in the solutions. Children can pool their solutions and become aware of more patterns.

Further extension
Cookies are packed into three sizes of box: yellow boxes of 5, pink boxes of 8 and green boxes of 11.
All the cookies must be packed into boxes with none left over. Try to get as close as possible to the same number of boxes of each colour. What is the best way to pack each of these quantities of cookies: 68?
(for example 6 yellow, 2 pink, 2 green) *102?* (for example 3 yellow, 4 pink, 5 green) *118?* (for example 6 yellow, 4 pink, 4 green).

If you have time
Discuss with children two boxes taking different quantities of goods. *Are there any numbers that cannot fit exactly in the boxes?* Is there always a largest number that cannot be used to fill boxes exactly?

Information
Where two numbers have no common factor other than 1, for example 5 and 8, then the largest number that cannot be made is (5 × 8) − (5 + 8). When there is a common factor other than 1, for example a box of 6 and a box of 9, there is not a largest number that does not fill the boxes exactly; any number which is not a multiple of 3 will not fit exactly.

Be aware

- The move from solving examples to searching for number patterns is a significant step up in difficulty. Small groups working together can give mutual support and share ideas.

Outcomes

- I can solve problems with several steps.
- I can explore and find patterns in my results.

Challenge Plan: Year 4

B1: number pairs to 100/1000; adding to next 100/1000; name, describe and visualise common shapes; polygons and types of triangles

Summary

Y4 ⬡ B1.1   **Extending number pairs**

A small group working with an adult

Year 4 Challenge Textbook page 8

Abacus Evolve objectives	Framework objectives
• Derive quickly pairs of numbers that total 100 • Derive quickly pairs of multiples of 5 that total 100 • Derive quickly pairs of multiples of 50 that total 1000	• Use knowledge of addition and subtraction facts and place value to derive sums and differences of pairs of multiples of 10, 100 or 1000

Teacher notes

Getting started
Consolidate understanding of number pairs with children:
• *Let's warm up with pairs to 1000.*
500 (500), 700 (300), 750 (250), 150 (850)

Activity
• *Let's try some pairs to 2000.*
1500 (500), 1300 (700), 1250 (750), 800 (1200)
• *Now let's try a few more pairs with different totals.*
We want to make 5000. What number pair do you need if you have 2000? (3000) If you have 4500? (500)
We want to make 8000. What number pair do you need if you have 4000? (4000) If you have 2500? (5500)
• *Let's look at some other numbers.*
We want to make 100. What number pair do you need if you have 20? (80)
We want to make 1000. What number pair do you need if you have 200? (800)
We want to make 10 000. What number pair do you need if you have 2000? (8000)

What do you notice? (Encourage answers relating to place value.)
Children work from Textbook page 8. They complete questions 1 to 8.

• *We can also make number pairs with fractions.*
We want to make 10. What number pair do you need if you have 2? (8)
We want to make 10. What number pair do you need if you have $2\frac{1}{2}$? ($7\frac{1}{2}$)
We want to make 10. What number pair do you need if you have $1\frac{1}{2}$? ($8\frac{1}{2}$)
We want to make 10. What number pair do you need if you have $2\frac{1}{4}$? ($7\frac{3}{4}$)

When children are confident working with number pairs with fractions, they complete the activity on the Textbook page.

Be aware	Outcomes
• Some children are confident naming numbers up to 9999, but may think that 10 000 is a million, or that 100 000 is a million. • Some children may not realise that number pairs can also apply to money and fractions, not just whole numbers.	• I can find number pairs for larger numbers, money and mixed whole numbers and fractions.

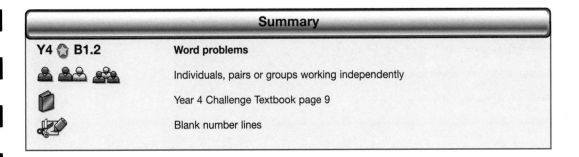

B1: number pairs to 100/1000; adding to next 100/1000; name, describe and visualise common shapes; polygons and types of triangles

Summary

Y4 ✪ B1.2

Word problems

Individuals, pairs or groups working independently

Year 4 Challenge Textbook page 9

Blank number lines

Abacus Evolve objectives

- Derive quickly pairs of numbers that total 100
- Derive quickly pairs of multiples of 5 that total 100
- Derive quickly pairs of multiples of 50 that total 1000

Framework objectives

- Use knowledge of addition and subtraction facts and place value to derive sums and differences of pairs of multiples of 10, 100 or 1000

Teacher notes

Activity
Children work from Textbook page 9. They solve word problems. Children consider each word problem and transfer it to a blank number line. They use a two jump strategy to solve it and then record the answer, making sure to return to the context of the word problem.

If you have time
The group can hand in any good word problems that they have devised themselves, so that these can be kept and used as a resource for the whole class.

Be aware

- Subtraction is seen as an abstract operation, without many everyday practical applications. Make sure children are aware that they are using subtraction to solve these word problems.

Outcomes

- I can solve two-step subtraction word problems.
- I can write my own subtraction word problems.

Challenge Plan: Year 4

Summary

Y4 ⭐ B1.3

Number pair game

A small group working with a teacher

Year 4 Challenge PCM 2

Abacus Evolve objectives

- Derive quickly pairs of numbers that total 100
- Derive quickly pairs of multiples of 5 that total 100
- Derive quickly pairs of multiples of 50 that total 1000
- Find what to add to a 2- or 3-digit number to make 100 or the next multiple of 100
- Find what to add to a 4-digit multiple of 100 to make the next multiple of 1000

Framework objectives

- Use knowledge of addition and subtraction facts and place value to derive sums and differences of pairs of multiples of 10, 100 or 1000

Teacher notes

Preparation
Photocopy and cut out the 24 playing cards on PCM 2. (If there are more than four children in the group, then make a second set of cards.) Separate the cards into four sets of six, set A, set B, set C and set D.

Getting started
Consolidate understanding of number pairs to multiples of 1000 with children.
We want to make 4000. What number pair do you need if you have 1000? (3000) *If you have 2500?* (1500)
We want to make 6000. What number pair do you need if you have 4000? (2000) *If you have 5500?* (500)

Activity
- Give each child or pair of children one set of six cards.
- The first child lays down the card with the face value of 245 (there is one of these in each set).
- That child solves the question on the card and links it to the correct answer on their next card, and so on to form a chain. Other children may help to solve the question if necessary.
- Repeat until each child has made a chain.
- When children have each completed one chain they swap cards until everyone has completed all four chains.
- Then shuffle all 24 cards together and deal them out.
- The first child lays down the card with the face value of 245.
- If the next child has the corresponding answer card they lay it down. If not they 'pass' to the next child.
- The winner is the first child to get rid of all their cards.

If you have time
Play again. Encourage children to be faster. Allow a 'Play when you can go' rule instead of taking turns.

Information
Any card in a set can be first in the chain as each set forms a loop of six cards.

Be aware

- Some children may make the error of finding pairs for some of the digits, but not for the whole number. They might try to pair 876 with 234 or 134 to reach 1000 rather than correctly pairing it with 124.

Outcomes

- I can quickly find number pairs up to 10000.

Supporting resources

You can find lots more loop card activities here:
- http://www.loopcards.net

Challenge Plan: Year 4

B1: number pairs to 100/1000; adding to next 100/1000; name, describe and visualise common shapes; polygons and types of triangles

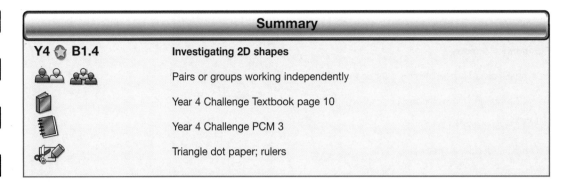

Summary

Y4 ☆ B1.4

Investigating 2D shapes

Pairs or groups working independently

Year 4 Challenge Textbook page 10

Year 4 Challenge PCM 3

Triangle dot paper; rulers

Abacus Evolve objectives

- **Y5** Rehearse the names and properties of common 2D shapes
- **Y5** Rehearse regular and irregular polygons

Framework objectives

- **Y5** Identify, visualise and describe properties of rectangles, triangles, regular polygons and 3D solids; use knowledge of properties to draw 2D shapes, and identify and draw nets of 3D shapes
- **Y5** Plan and pursue an enquiry; present evidence by collecting, organising and interpreting information; suggest extensions to the enquiry

Teacher notes

Preparation
Photocopy PCM 3 onto thin card and cut out the shapes. Each child should have two of each shape.

Getting started
Look together at the diamond on the Textbook page. Briefly discuss how it is one shape made from joining two smaller shapes together. Ask children to point out the two triangles that make up the diamond. Stress the importance of the matching edges.

Activity
Children work from Textbook page 10. They join the shapes (two diamonds and two equilateral triangles) together to make new shapes. Children draw their new shapes on triangle dot paper. They then explore how many sides each new shape has and how many equilateral triangles each shape is composed from. Children should be encouraged to share and compare results.

If you have time
Point out that the original shapes have just two sizes of angle. *The larger angle is twice as big as the smaller angle.* Children work together to explore angle totals for their new shapes and explain any patterns that they find. (Patterns will arise from the fact that the triangle has three small angles and the diamond has two small angles and two large angles.)

Information
'Diamond' is the mathematical name for a rhombus made from two equilateral triangles.

Be aware

- Children should be encouraged to explore possible 2D shapes and their properties using systematic thinking. They may be interested in the names of the shapes they generate but this is less important in the context of this activity.

Outcomes

- I can join 2D shapes together to make new 2D shapes.
- I can think about 2D shapes and their properties.
- I can record what I have found out about the 2D shapes I made.

Supporting resources

Look at more tile patterns here:
- http://www.mathpuzzle.com/tilepent.html

B1: number pairs to 100/1000; adding to next 100/1000; name, describe and visualise common shapes; polygons and types of triangles

Summary

Y4 ⬟ B1.5

Rotational symmetry

Individuals, pairs or groups working independently

Year 4 Challenge Textbook page 11

Year 4 Challenge PCM 4

2 cm square dot paper; rulers

Abacus Evolve objectives

- Rehearse the concept of line symmetry
- Classify polygons according to their lines of symmetry
- Make and investigate a general statement about familiar numbers or shapes by finding examples that satisfy it (shape)

Framework objectives

- Draw polygons and classify them by identifying their properties, including their line symmetry
- Identify and use patterns, relationships and properties of numbers or shapes; investigate a statement involving numbers and test it with examples

Teacher notes

Getting started
Photocopy PCM 4, one per child.

Activity
Children work from Textbook page 11. Children draw lines to bisect the parallelogram on PCM 4, recognising that these are not lines of symmetry. Where the lines cross children find the centre of rotational symmetry of this shape. They rotate the shape about its centre to recognise its rotational symmetry. Children investigate the rotational symmetry of the five other shapes and designs. They then extend to look at four more complex designs. Children choose the odd one out which does not have rotational symmetry.

If you have time
Children make their own design which has rotational symmetry.

Information
Rotational symmetry is at least as important as reflection and line symmetry. It is essential in most objects that rotate and is linked to the wheel or other cyclic objects. It is important for children to recognise that reflection and rotational symmetry are just the start of a wide range of other forms of symmetry.

Be aware

- Children may think that line symmetry is different from symmetry. Ensure children understand that they are the same and that these two phrases can be used interchangeably. Make sure, however, that they recognise that rotational symmetry is a different concept.

Outcomes

- I can recognise rotational symmetry.
- I can find out if a shape has rotational symmetry.

Supporting resources

Hub caps, manhole covers, road signs, windmills, wind pumps and wind turbines are all real-life examples of shapes that may have rotational symmetry. Look here for pictures of these items for children to explore:
- http://images.google.co.uk/

Find out more about rotational symmetry on the internet:
- www.mystery-productions.info/hyper/Hypermedia_1999/BENTON/index.htm

Challenge Plan: Year 4

B1: number pairs to 100/1000; adding to next 100/1000; name, describe and visualise common shapes; polygons and types of triangles

Summary

Y4 ⬡ B1.6

2D shape patterns

Pairs or groups working independently

Year 4 Challenge Textbook page 12

Year 4 Challenge PCM 5

Abacus Evolve objectives

- **Y5** Classify triangles, using criteria such as equal sides, equal angles, lines of symmetry

Framework objectives

- **Y5** Identify, visualise and describe properties of rectangles, triangles, regular polygons and 3D solids; use knowledge of properties to draw 2D shapes, and to identify and draw nets of 3D shapes

Teacher notes

Getting started
Children should be familiar with the characteristics of four types of triangles; right-angled, scalene, isosceles and equilateral. Give children a chance to discuss these before they start the activity.

Activity
Children work from Textbook page 12. They look at a crazy paving pattern of seven different triangles and consider the similarities and differences between the triangles.
- Children complete a table on PCM 5, with the properties of the different scalene triangles.
- They then complete a table with the properties of the other types of triangles.
- Children discuss a crazy paving pattern of different quadrilaterals and note the qualities of each quadrilateral.

If you have time
Ask *Why is a square also a rectangle?* (A square is a rectangle because it is a quadrilateral with four sides and four right angles. We call it a square to show that all its sides are equal lengths.)

Be aware

- Children may not recognise that scalene triangles have distinguishing properties.
- Scalene triangles and isosceles triangles can both be right-angled triangles. Equilateral triangles cannot be right-angled triangles.
- Every square is a rectangle, however not every rectangle is a square.

Outcomes

- I can describe the properties of different triangles.
- I can recognise and describe the properties of quadrilaterals.

Challenge Plan: Year 4

C1: standard metric units of length; area; tally charts and frequency tables; pictograms

Summary

Y4 ⬡ C1.1

Imperial units

Pairs or groups working independently

Year 4 Challenge Textbook page 13

Abacus Evolve objectives

- Begin to use imperial units of length: miles
- Begin to use imperial units of capacity: pints

Framework objectives

- *Choose and use standard metric units and their abbreviations when estimating, measuring and recording length, weight and capacity; know the meaning of 'kilo', 'centi' and 'milli' and, where appropriate, use decimal notation to record measurements (e.g. 1·3 m or 0·6 kg)*
- Solve one-step and two-step problems involving numbers, money or measures, including time; choose and carry out appropriate calculations, using calculator methods where appropriate

Teacher notes

Activity

Children work from Textbook page 13. They read about imperial and metric units of measurement, and then work in pairs to find approximate conversions between imperial and metric measures. The Textbook page shows them a grid format which may help them with their conversions. Children then work in pairs to make up some similar word problems of their own, involving other roughly equivalent measurements. Pairs can then swap problems and solve each other's.

If you have time

Ask the group to agree on the best problems created and design their own worksheet for other children to use.

Information

Some useful approximate conversions between metric and imperial measures are:

4 litres ≈ 7 pints	9 litres ≈ 2 gallons or 16 pints
5 kilograms ≈ 11 pounds	30 grams ≈ 1 ounce
8 kilometres ≈ 5 miles	

Some more accurate conversions are:

4 litres ≈ 7·04 pints	9 litres ≈ 15·85 pints
5 kilograms ≈ 11·02 pounds	28·35 grams ≈ 1 ounce
8·05 kilometres ≈ 5 miles	2·54 cm = 1 inch

Be aware

- Proportional reasoning can be challenging but children can be supported in this by securing the problem firmly within a real-life context.

Outcomes

- I can solve word problems about converting measures.
- I can make up word problems about converting measures.
- I can make rough conversions between imperial and metric units.

Supporting resources

Children can do conversions between imperial and metric at:
- www.day-tripper.net/infoconversions.html#Anchorconversion

This website gives some more accurate conversions:
- www.nwml.gov.uk/faqs.aspx?id=8

Summary

Y4 ⭐ C1.2   **Pairs of tetrominoes**

Pairs or groups working independently

Year 4 Challenge Textbook page 14

Card tetromino sets; 2 cm squared dot paper if possible (1 cm squared dot paper if not)

Abacus Evolve objectives

- **Y5** Understand, measure and calculate perimeters of rectangles
- **Y5** Understand and use the formula in words 'length × breadth' for the area of a rectangle

Framework objectives

- **Y5** *Draw and measure lines to the nearest millimetre; measure and calculate the perimeter of regular and irregular polygons; use the formula for the area of a rectangle to calculate the rectangle's area*
- **Y5** Explain reasoning using diagrams, graphs and text; refine ways of recording using images and symbols

Teacher notes

Preparation
Prepare card sets of tetrominoes (as on Textbook page 14) for each child, to fit 2 cm or 1 cm squared dot paper.

Activity
Children work from Textbook page 14. They are introduced to the idea of a tetromino and are shown the five possible tetrominoes. They explore the perimeter of each one, using the idea of 1 cm 'steps' and walking around the sides of the shape. The area of each tetromino is 4 cm² and the perimeter is 10 cm for all but one, where it is 8 cm.

Next children fit pairs of tetrominoes together to make composite shapes. They draw these on dot paper, and find and record the area and perimeter of each. They investigate the minimum and maximum perimeters that can be made.

Further extension
Ask children to investigate the area and perimeters of pentiamonds (shapes made from five equilateral triangles), and of composite shapes made using them. Avoid extending the activity to pentominoes (five squares), as they are investigated later in the year, in B2.

Be aware

- Children often confuse area and perimeter and so may be surprised that these vary independently.
- The more compact the shape the smaller the perimeter. You could link this to the concept of small mammals curling up tightly to minimise their surface area (3D equivalent of perimeter).

Outcomes

- I can find the perimeters of different shapes with the same area.
- I can explore all the possible pairs and arrangements of these shapes systematically.

Supporting resources

For advanced puzzling with tetrominoes see:
- www.martinhwatson.co.uk/tetrominoes.html

Summary

Y4 ✦ C1.3

Areas of rectangles

A group of children working with an adult

Year 4 Challenge Textbook page 15

Year 4 Challenge PCM 6

Thin card; scissors; 2 cm squared paper; squared dot paper (optional)

Abacus Evolve objectives

- Understand area as 'covering' in two dimensions
- Measure area using non-standard units
- Measure area using standard units: square centimeters

Framework objectives

- Draw rectangles and measure and calculate their perimeters; find the area of rectilinear shapes drawn on a square grid by counting squares
- Identify and use patterns, relationships and properties of numbers or shapes; investigate a statement involving numbers and test it with examples
- Represent a puzzle or problem using number sentences, statements or diagrams; use these to solve the problem; present and interpret the solution in the context of the problem

Teacher notes

Preparation
Photocopy PCM 6 onto thin card, one copy per child.

Activity
- Children work from Textbook page 15. *What is the area of a 1 by 2 rectangle?* (2 square units) *What is the area of a 3 by 4 rectangle?* (12 square units) *These are called 'oblong numbers'.*
- Children investigate other rectangles with oblong number areas. *How are you going to record your results?* Suggest using tables and explain the importance of organising and being systematic in the investigation. *What patterns can you see?* Discuss the results as a group.
- *A square is a type of rectangle!* Systematically explore and discuss the areas of squares, as above.
- Think about and explore the areas of rectangles where one pair of sides is two units longer than the other.
- Ask children to compare and discuss their results for the third type of rectangle with their results for the squares. *What do you notice? Is there a connection between similar sized rectangle and square areas?*

Information
A square number is 1 more than the product of the numbers that are one more and one less than the root number: $n^2 = (n + 1)(n - 1) + 1$.

Be aware

- Children may need help in recording systematically, for example in tables. If they do not work in a systematic way the patterns in their results may be hard to see.

Outcomes

- I can find areas of rectangles.
- I can find the differences in a sequence of areas.
- I can follow a pattern and predict the next numbers.
- I can see links between two patterns.

Supporting resources

Explore square numbers and roots further at:
- www.ickids.org.uk/sats/number_squares.htm

Summary

Y4 ⬡ C1.4

Showing data in different ways

Groups working independently

Year 4 Challenge PCM 7

Squared or graph paper; internet (optional)

Abacus Evolve objectives

- **Y5** Draw and interpret frequency tables, pictograms and bar graphs

Framework objectives

- **Y5** *Construct frequency tables, pictograms and bar and line graphs to represent the frequencies of events and changes over time*

Teacher notes

Getting started
Photocopy PCM 7, one per child. Provide suitable paper for constructing their tables and graphs.

Activity
Children read the information from PCM 7 and decide how to organise the data. They then construct frequency tables based on the two sets of data.
Children create a pictogram and a bar graph representing the small car data and the large car data. They compare the two types of graph and consider which type of graph is more useful for representing these sets of data.

Further extension
Children can directly compare the journeys to see if there is a pattern to the carbon costs of the two cars.
They may recognise that 'half as much again' is used by the larger car.

If you have time
Children can use the internet to find the carbon cost of real journeys and real cars.

Information
Carbon costs are estimated for car journeys on some internet map directions sites.

Be aware

- The idea of a carbon cost to travel and a carbon footprint is a challenging one but children should be able to understand it.
- When comparing data, children often look for a pattern in the differences between number values rather than for a proportional increase like there is in this data.

Outcomes

- I can make a frequency table by grouping my data.
- I can change this table into a picture or graph.
- I can compare different pictures of the same data.

Supporting resources

Enter a journey into Multimap and you can see the carbon footprint for different types of car:
- www.multimap.com/directions

C1: standard metric units of length; area; tally charts and frequency tables; pictograms

Summary

Y4 ⬡ C1.5

All sorts of bears

A group of children working with an adult

Year 4 Challenge Textbook page 16

Year 4 Challenge PCM 8

The internet or reference books about bears

Abacus Evolve objectives

- Represent data in frequency tables

Framework objectives

- *Answer a question by identifying what data to collect; organise, present, analyse and interpret the data in tables, diagrams, tally charts, pictograms and bar charts, using ICT where appropriate*
- Suggest a line of enquiry and the strategy needed to follow it; collect, organise and interpret selected information to find answers

Teacher notes

Preparation
Photocopy PCM 8 and cut out the cards. Give each pair of children a few bears to investigate.

Activity
- PCM 8 has some data about different kinds of bears.
- Children work from Textbook page 16. With the data from PCM 8 as a starting point they use the internet or reference books to find out more about their types of bear. They add the information they find onto the cards.
- The group discuss what questions could be asked to identify each bear. The questions must have *yes* or *no* answers. (They are likely to be about distinguishing features, eating habits, habitat, and so on.) Together they compile a list of eight questions that allows them to identify any of their bears.
- Children use the data cards to play a game. One child picks a bear in secret. The others ask the agreed questions until the bear is identified.

Information
Binary questions with just a *yes* or *no* answer are the basis for all computer systems of data storage.

Be aware

- Children may be unaware of the sorting power of yes/no questions and so may want to include more questions. However the restriction in the number of questions encourages them to think more carefully about which are the best questions to choose.

Outcomes

- I can find out data about a type of animal.
- I can put my data about a particular animal onto a data card.
- I can ask good questions about a set of animals to help to sort them out into different types.

Supporting resources

Look for more bear information under 'animal printouts' at:
- www.enchantedlearning.com

Bear facts, further links and pictures, can be found by searching for 'bear' at:
- http://www.bbc.co.uk/nature/wildfacts/

Challenge Plan: Year 4

C1: standard metric units of length; area; tally charts and frequency tables; pictograms

Summary

Y4 ⭐ C1.6	**Make your own pictograms**
👥	Groups working independently
📖	Year 4 Challenge Textbook page 17
✂️✏️	Squared or graph paper

Abacus Evolve objectives

- Construct and interpret pictograms where the symbol represents 2, 5, 10 or 20 units
- Represent data in frequency tables
- Interpret tally charts and frequency tables

Framework objectives

- Compare the impact of representations where scales have intervals of differing step size
- *Answer a question by identifying what data to collect; organise, present, analyse and interpret the data in tables, diagrams, tally charts, pictograms and bar charts, using ICT where appropriate*
- Suggest a line of enquiry and the strategy needed to follow it; collect, organise and interpret selected information to find answers

Teacher notes

Preparation
Check that children understand the data in the two tables on Textbook page 17.

Activity
Children work from Textbook page 17. They use data to produce a frequency table. From this, they produce a pictogram. Children look at their pictogram and discuss what they can see from the graph that was not clear from the table.
Children then use the second table of data on the page and produce another pictogram which they compare with their first one.

Be aware

- Make sure children are aware that they have the choice of what symbols to use for their pictogram and what number each symbol can represent. Highlight the importance of choosing a sensible scale.

Outcomes

- I can use data to make a frequency table.
- I can use data to make a pictogram with a good scale.

Supporting resources

This is a website where pictograms can be made online using your own data:
- gwydir.demon.co.uk/jo/numbers/pictogram/info.htm

Challenge Plan: Year 4

D1: add several small numbers; add and subtract multiples of 10 or 100; analogue and 24-hour clocks; seconds and minutes

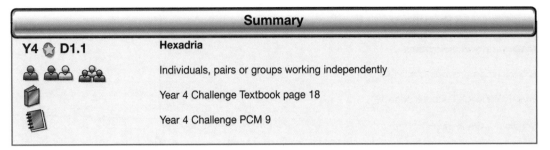

Summary

Y4 ⬡ D1.1

Hexadria

Individuals, pairs or groups working independently

Year 4 Challenge Textbook page 18

Year 4 Challenge PCM 9

Abacus Evolve objectives

- Check the sum of several numbers by adding in reverse order
- Add several multiples of 10 or 100
- Derive quickly pairs of numbers that total 100
- Derive quickly pairs of multiples of 5 that total 100

Framework objectives

- Use knowledge of addition and subtraction facts and place value to derive sums and differences of pairs of multiples of 10, 100 or 1000
- Suggest a line of enquiry and the strategy needed to follow it; collect, organise and interpret selected information to find answers
- Report solutions to puzzles and problems, giving explanations and reasoning orally and in writing, using diagrams and symbols

Teacher notes

Preparation
Photocopy PCM 9, one copy per child.

Activity
Children work from Textbook page 18. They begin by exploring sets of three multiples of 5 that total 100, using the structure of a hexagon divided into three rhombuses. They then explore pairs of multiples of 5 that total 100, using the structure of a cube whose opposite faces must add to 100.
Children then move on to look at hexadria. A hexadrian is a hexagon made up of six overlapping smaller hexagons. The rule is that the numbers on the three rhombuses of each small hexagon must add to the same total. Children use multiples of 5 up to 95 and aim to make each small hexagon total 100. Children try to make successful hexadria, and investigate what the six numbers in the centre add up to.

Here is an example solution.
Note that the centre star of numbers total 105.

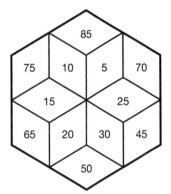

Further extension
Allow children to use other numbers to create different totals. Children can use examples that they create to set up problems to give to others in the group. For example, the totals of each hexagon may be 80, with a central ring total of 120.

Be aware

- Some children may initially find it difficult to investigate in such an open situation. They may need more prompts or direction in the early stages.

Outcomes

- I can find several multiples of 5 and 10 that add to 100.
- I can solve number problems.

D1: add several small numbers; add and subtract multiples of 10 or 100; analogue and 24-hour clocks; seconds and minutes

Summary

Y4 ⭐ D1.2

Adding consecutive numbers

A group of children working with an adult

Year 4 Challenge Textbook page 19

Abacus Evolve objectives

- **Y5** Continue to add several 1-digit numbers
- **Y5** Check the sum of several numbers by adding in reverse order
- **Y5** Make general statements about odd or even numbers, including their sums and differences
- **Y5** Explain a generalised relationship (formula) in words
- **Y5** Recognise and explain patterns and relationships, generalise and predict

Framework objectives

- **Y5** *Use efficient written methods to add and subtract whole numbers and decimals with up to two places*
- **Y5** Represent a puzzle or problem by identifying and recording the information or calculations needed to solve it; find possible solutions and confirm them in the context of the problem
- **Y5** Plan and pursue an enquiry; present evidence by collecting, organising and interpreting information; suggest extensions to the enquiry

Teacher notes

Activity

Children work from Textbook page 19. They start off in pairs, investigating the result of adding two consecutive numbers, and describing the pattern. They move on to three consecutive numbers, then larger sets of consecutive numbers. They try to write rules for the answer to each size set of numbers. When pairs have finished exploring each size set of numbers, encourage children to discuss their results as a group.

Children then move on to finding answers that can be made in more than one way. They are shown the example that 9 is the smallest number that can be made in two ways: 4 + 5 and 2 + 3 + 4. Children investigate what is the smallest number that can be made in three different ways, and then in four different ways.

Information

Odd numbers of consecutive numbers add to a multiple of that number. For example, adding three consecutive numbers always leads to a multiple of 3; five consecutive numbers total a multiple of 5. Even numbers of consecutive numbers are different. Two consecutive numbers always add to an odd number. Four consecutive numbers always add to 2 more than a multiple of 4. For six numbers, you get 3 more than a multiple of 6.

Be aware

- Children may see patterns as 'how the numbers go up' but not at first recognise the general pattern of multiples. They may need to be prompted to look for reasons and to find the general pattern. If they work as a group, they may find the patterns without intervention from an adult.

Outcomes

- I can solve problems by investigating systematically.
- I can see patterns in the answers from an investigation.
- I can find general rules and reasons for these.

Supporting resources

Further resources on adding consecutive numbers can be found at:
- nrich.maths.org/public/viewer.php?obj_id=507
- www.jaconline.com.au/mathsquestnsw/mq7nsw/investigations/2003-09-08-consec.pdf

D1: add several small numbers; add and subtract multiples of 10 or 100; analogue and 24-hour clocks; seconds and minutes

Summary

Y4 ⬥ D1.3

Adding and subtracting near decades

Pairs or groups working independently

Year 4 Challenge PCM 10

Abacus Evolve objectives

- Add and subtract 2- and 3-digit multiples of 10
- Add near multiples of 10 to 2- and 3-digit numbers

Framework objectives

- Use knowledge of addition and subtraction facts and place value to derive sums and differences of pairs of multiples of 10, 100 or 1000
- *Add or subtract mentally pairs of 2-digit whole numbers (e.g. 47 + 58, 91 − 35)*

Teacher notes

Getting started
Explain to children that they should aim to solve the calculations in their heads (but jotting down workings, or using an empty number line is okay if they need to). Encourage children to discuss and write about the strategies they are using.

Activity
Children work from PCM 10. They start off by solving some missing-number calculations involving adding and subtracting multiples of 10. They then move on to adding and subtracting near multiples of 10, building up to some more complex examples.

If you have time
Children can set challenges for each other by making up further problems using 3-digit numbers.

Be aware

- Some children find it difficult to stick with a taught strategy especially if they can easily see another way to solve the simpler examples. They may need encouragement to stick with the strategy so that they can use it on the harder examples later on.

Outcomes

- I can add and subtract multiples of 10.
- I can adjust known facts to find nearby facts.

Challenge Plan: Year 4

D1: add several small numbers; add and subtract multiples of 10 or 100; analogue and 24-hour clocks; seconds and minutes

Summary

Y4 ✪ D1.4

Before and after the hour

Groups working independently

Year 4 Challenge Textbook page 20

Year 4 Challenge PCM 11

Thin card

Abacus Evolve objectives

- Use known number facts and place value to add two 2-digit numbers, adding the tens first
- Use am and pm and the notation 9:53

Framework objectives

- *Add or subtract mentally pairs of two-digit whole numbers (e.g. 47 + 58, 91 − 35)*
- Read time to the nearest minute; use am, pm and 12-hour clock notation; choose units of time to measure time intervals; calculate time intervals from clocks and timetables

Teacher notes

Preparation
Photocopy PCM 11 onto thin card. Cut out the 24 playing cards. If the group contains more than four children, make two sets.

Activity
Children work from Textbook page 20. To familiarise themselves with the cards before beginning to play the game, each child or pair of children takes one set of six cards and practises making a chain of times. They repeat for a different set.
Then they play the game. They shuffle all 24 cards together and deal them out between the members of the group. One child with a 9:45 card puts that card down first. Children take turns to look at their cards and put one down on top of the previous card if they have the next card in the chain. If they do not have the next card, they pass on their go. Children continue doing this, checking each time that the correct card has been played. The winner is the first child to get rid of all their cards.
The group then plays the game again, trying to do it faster than before. Then they play again. This time they do not take turns, but place the next card as soon as they can.

Be aware

- Children may not realise at first that the four sets of six cards create a continuous loop – they may think that the game has to be stopped when the end of one chain is reached.

Outcomes

- I can quickly and accurately find the pair for any number adding up to 60 minutes.
- I can quickly and accurately find the time earlier or later when crossing the hour.

Supporting resources

For more card games of this kind see:
- www.loopcards.net

Challenge Plan: Year 4

D1: add several small numbers; add and subtract multiples of 10 or 100; analogue and 24-hour clocks; seconds and minutes

Summary

Y4 ✪ D1.5

Fractions of 60

A group of children working with an adult

Year 4 Challenge Textbook page 21

Abacus Evolve objectives

- **Y5** Convert from one unit of time to another
- **Y5** Relate fractions to division
- **Y5** Use division to find fractions, including tenths and hundredths of numbers and quantities

Framework objectives

- **Y5** Read timetables and time using 24-hour clock notation; use a calendar to calculate time intervals
- **Y5** Find fractions using division (e.g. $\frac{1}{100}$ of 5 kg), and percentages of numbers and quantities (e.g. 10%, 5% and 15% of £80)

Teacher notes

Getting started
Introduce the idea of fractions of 60 by asking what fractions of 60 children can suggest. They are likely to suggest $\frac{1}{2}$, $\frac{1}{4}$ and $\frac{3}{4}$, but may also bring in $\frac{1}{3}$, $\frac{1}{6}$, $\frac{1}{10}$ and other fractions.
Refer to the three examples of '60' on Textbook page 21, to confirm their suggestions for fractions of 60. Children can use these examples to help them to think about the fractions or to confirm their working.

Activity
Children work from Textbook page 21. They match up fractions of an hour with numbers of minutes. They will find that there are a few fractions on the page that do not match a number of minutes, and a few numbers of minutes that do not have a matching fraction. For these they are challenged to find the partner number or fraction.
The unpaired fractions are: $\frac{3}{4}$, $\frac{3}{5}$, $\frac{7}{10}$, $\frac{5}{12}$ and $\frac{1}{20}$. Their missing partners are 45, 36, 42, 25 and 3.
The unpaired numbers are: 24, 48, 18, 5 and 9. Their missing partners are $\frac{2}{5}$, $\frac{4}{5}$, $\frac{3}{10}$, $\frac{1}{12}$, and $\frac{3}{20}$.

Information
The ancient Middle Eastern civilisation of Babylon used 60 as a key number. Their place value system was based on 60 rather than 10 and six 60s were used to make the 360 degrees in a complete turn. The 60 seconds in a minute and 60 minutes in an hour are inherited from Babylonian mathematics.

Be aware

- As children will be familiar with decimal systems, the 60 system can lead to errors.
- Times are often written to look like decimals, for example 11·45, which can lead to confusion.

Outcomes

- I can find fractions of 60 minutes using division.
- I can recognise when fractions are equivalent.

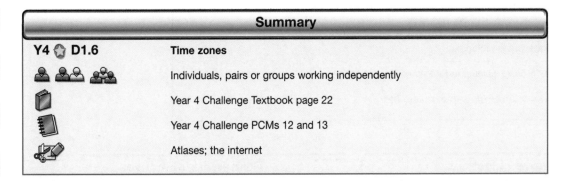

Challenge Plan: Year 4

D1: add several small numbers; add and subtract multiples of 10 or 100; analogue and 24-hour clocks; seconds and minutes

Summary

Y4 ⭐ D1.6

Time zones

Individuals, pairs or groups working independently

Year 4 Challenge Textbook page 22

Year 4 Challenge PCMs 12 and 13

Atlases; the internet

Abacus Evolve objectives

- Estimate and measure time using seconds, minutes, hours
- Rehearse time to the nearest minute on 12-hour digital clocks
- Read the time to the nearest minute on analogue clocks
- Use am and pm and the notation 9:53

Framework objectives

- Read time to the nearest minute; use am, pm and 12-hour clock notation; choose units of time to measure time intervals; calculate time intervals from clocks and timetables

Teacher notes

Preparation
Photocopy PCM 12 one copy per child.

Activity
Children work from Textbook page 22 and PCM 12. They read about the introduction of standard time zones. Children look at a table showing a journey around the world, travelling east, and plot this journey on the world time zones map on PCM 13. They then look at an incomplete table for a journey around the world travelling west. They use atlases or the internet and refer to the world time zones map on PCM 13 to complete the table for a journey of their choice.

If you have time
Children can use the weblink below to make their own time zone maps, putting relatives or their favourite celebrities on the map. They can then check it to see what time it is for those people.

Be aware

- While children may be aware of some aspects of world time – for example the International Date Line – they may not have connected these together into a coherent picture before.

Outcomes

- I can find the time zone for different countries around the world.
- I can work out how time zones change in a journey around the world.
- I understand how lines of longitude are linked to time zones.

Supporting resources

Children can make their own time zone maps using this website:
- www.zebramap.com

Challenge Plan: Year 4

E1: count in 2s, 3s, 4s, 5s, 10s, 25s, 50s; multiplication and division facts; fractions and mixed numbers; equivalent simple fractions

Summary

Y4 ⭐ E1.1

Patterns in multiples

Individuals, pairs or groups working independently

Year 4 Challenge Textbook page 23

Abacus Evolve objectives

- Recognise multiples of 2, 3, 4, 5 and 10, up to the tenth multiple
- Know by heart the multiplication facts for the 2, 3, 4, 5 and 10 times tables
- Recognise and explain patterns and relationships, generalise and predict
- Make and investigate a general statement about familiar numbers or shapes by finding examples that satisfy it (number)

Framework objectives

- *Derive and recall multiplication facts up to 10 × 10, the corresponding division facts and multiples of numbers to 10 up to the tenth multiple*
- Identify and use patterns, relationships and properties of numbers or shapes; investigate a statement involving numbers and test it with examples
- Report solutions to puzzles and problems, giving explanations and reasoning orally and in writing, using diagrams and symbols

Teacher notes

Getting started

Show children Textbook page 23 and check that they all understand how the diagram works.

Activity

Children work from Textbook page 23. They read about G.H. Hardy and number theory, and look at a diagram showing the pattern of final digits when multiplying by 2. Children then investigate the patterns for multiplying by other numbers (4, 8, 1, 5, 3, 6, 7 and 9) and try to draw diagrams to show what they have found.

If you have time

Children can discuss the patterns they have found and share ideas.

Information

The ×4 pattern can be found by following two arrow journeys on the doubling diagram. Children should notice that the patterns for ×2 and ×8 are very similar, with the cycle of four numbers at its centre being reversed. This also happens with ×3 and ×7. These similarities occur because 2 and 8, 3 and 7 are pairs that make 10.

Be aware

- Children may be unfamiliar with using arrow notation to indicate a relationship. Check that they are following the diagram accurately.

Outcomes

- I can explore and record patterns in numbers.
- I can find general patterns when multiplying.

Challenge Plan: Year 4

E1: count in 2s, 3s, 4s, 5s, 10s, 25s, 50s; multiplication and division facts; fractions and mixed numbers; equivalent simple fractions

Summary

Y4 E1.2

Sum, difference and product

A group of children working with an adult

Year 4 Challenge PCM 14

Calculators; paper

Abacus Evolve objectives

- **Y5** Use knowledge of sums or differences of odd/even numbers to check calculations

Framework objectives

- **Y5** Use knowledge of rounding, place value, number facts and inverse operations to estimate and check calculations
- **Y5** Solve one-step and two-step problems involving whole numbers and decimals and all four operations, choosing and using appropriate calculation strategies, including calculator use

Teacher notes

Preparation
Photocopy PCM 14, two copies per child or pair.

Activity
Write:
The two numbers are 7 and 3.
Their sum is ___
Their difference is ___
Their product is ___
Ask the group to work out the sum, difference and product. Discuss the fact that children were able to work these out mentally.

Show children PCM 14. Explain that: M = mental; P = pencil and paper; C = calculator. Demonstrate how to fill in one of the boxes for the numbers 7 and 3. Show that you circle 'M' to show that children worked it out mentally.

Give each child or pair a copy of PCM 14. Ask them to fill in the boxes by choosing a pair of numbers for each and filling in the sum, difference and product for each pair. They can do simple ones that can be solved mentally, more complex ones that may require a pencil and paper, and difficult ones that require a calculator. Then give each child or pair a new copy of the PCM. Ask them to copy out their sets of numbers, but only fill in three of the numbers for each calculation. For each set, they should circle the correct letter to show the level of difficulty.

Children then swap sheets and try to solve each other's.

Be aware

- Some problems involving difference – as against subtraction – can lead to more than one solution. Starting with 10, a number with a difference of two is either 8 or 12. The use of difference here can help the children to develop their use of difference.

Outcomes

- I can make good number problems.
- I can solve number problems made up by my group.

Challenge Plan: Year 4

E1: count in 2s, 3s, 4s, 5s, 10s, 25s, 50s; multiplication and division facts; fractions and mixed numbers; equivalent simple fractions

Summary

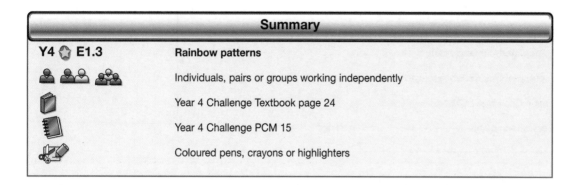

Y4 ⭐ E1.3

Rainbow patterns

Individuals, pairs or groups working independently

Year 4 Challenge Textbook page 24

Year 4 Challenge PCM 15

Coloured pens, crayons or highlighters

Abacus Evolve objectives

- Know by heart the multiplication facts for the 2, 3, 4, 5 and 10 times tables
- Recognise multiples of 2, 3, 4, 5 and 10, up to the tenth multiple
- Understand and use the commutativity of multiplication
- Recognise and explain patterns and relationships, generalise and predict

Framework objectives

- *Derive and recall multiplication facts up to 10 × 10, the corresponding division facts and multiples of numbers to 10 up to the tenth multiple*
- Identify and use patterns, relationships and properties of numbers or shapes; investigate a statement involving numbers and test it with examples

Teacher notes

Preparation
Photocopy PCM 15, one copy per child or pair.
Children will need to be familiar with using multiplication squares.

Activity
Children work from Textbook page 24. They look at the pattern of multiplications that have the product 20 and a list of the four multiplications that result in 20. They draw the pattern on the larger multiplication square on PCM 15. Children look for other numbers that occur five times or more within the multiplication square on the PCM. For example: 24, 30, 36, ..., 144. They colour each product in a different colour and record the multiplications for each product in a list. They are then asked to imagine that the multiplication square is extended even further and to think about where products they have already found would appear again in an extended grid.

Be aware

- The task is about recognising and interpreting multiplication patterns rather than simply multiplying.

Outcomes

- I can list pairs of numbers that give the same product.
- I can see how a set of multiplications are related.

Challenge Plan: Year 4

E1: count in 2s, 3s, 4s, 5s, 10s, 25s, 50s; multiplication and division facts; fractions and mixed numbers; equivalent simple fractions

Summary

Y4 ✦ E1.4	**Doubling and halving with fractions**
	Pairs or groups working independently
	Year 4 Challenge Textbook page 25

Abacus Evolve objectives

- Recognise mixed numbers
- Recognise the equivalence of simple fractions
- Begin to relate fractions to division
- Find fractions of numbers, quantities and shapes
- Use doubling or halving to find new facts from known facts

Framework objectives

- Use diagrams to identify equivalent fractions (e.g. $\frac{6}{8}$ and $\frac{3}{4}$, or $\frac{70}{100}$ and $\frac{7}{10}$); interpret mixed numbers and position them on a number line (e.g. $3\frac{1}{2}$)
- Find fractions of numbers, quantities or shapes (e.g. $\frac{1}{5}$ of 30 plums, $\frac{3}{8}$ of a 6 by 4 rectangle)
- Identify the doubles of 2-digit numbers; use these to calculate doubles of multiples of 10 and 100 and derive the corresponding halves

Teacher notes

Getting started

Go through the top part of the Textbook page together to make sure children understand how to find new multiplications by doubling one multiplier and halving the other.

Activity

Children work from Textbook page 25. Children start from given multiplications, for example 6 × 4, then double one number and halve the other several times to find new multiplications with the same product. They write these multiplications in tables. They will soon reach multiplications involving mixed numbers. After constructing these tables, they create some of their own. Children then copy and complete three tables in which they start with a multiplication involving a mixed number, and double/halve the multipliers until they get back to a multiplication involving two whole-number multipliers.

Be aware

- Children may not initially understand that a fraction multiplied by a whole number can be read as that fraction *of* the whole number. For example, $\frac{3}{4}$ × 32 is three quarters of thirty-two.

Outcomes

- I can find new multiplication facts by doubling and halving.
- I can create multiplications using mixed numbers.

Challenge Plan: Year 4

E1: count in 2s, 3s, 4s, 5s, 10s, 25s, 50s; multiplication and division facts; fractions and mixed numbers; equivalent simple fractions

Summary

Y4 ☆ E1.5

Fraction games

A group working with an adult

Year 4 Challenge Textbook page 26

Three sheets of paper (optional); 72 multilink cubes (optional); counters (optional)

Abacus Evolve objectives

- Identify two simple fractions with a total of 1
- Recognise simple fractions that are several parts of a whole
- Recognise the equivalence of simple fractions
- Locate fractions on a number line

Framework objectives

- Identify pairs of fractions that total 1
- Use diagrams to identify equivalent fractions (e.g. $\frac{6}{8}$ and $\frac{3}{4}$, or $\frac{70}{100}$ and $\frac{7}{10}$); interpret mixed numbers and position them on a number line (e.g. $3\frac{1}{2}$)

Teacher notes

Activity

Children work from Textbook page 26. They see three sets of numbers: one in grubs, one in frogs and one in a pool. They must add each grub number to a frog number to make a pool number. All the numbers must be used, and none can be used more than once. Encourage children to record their sets as number sentences and encourage them to work systematically. They then move on to the second part of the activity: they must subtract each grub number from a frog number to make a number in the second pool.

Extra help

Children may need an example at the start of the activity to clarify the way the numbers from grubs, frogs and the pool are matched.
You may need to support children if they find some of the fractions difficult to add. Fraction number lines are recommended based on the empty number line approach.

If you have time

Set out three sheets of paper to represent three rooms, and six sets of 12 multilink cubes in a 2 by 6 block. *Each cube is a piece of treasure.* The cubes are placed 'in' the rooms, with one block in the first room, two in the second room and three in the third room. Each player has two counters. The aim of the game is to end up with as much treasure as possible. In turn, players choose which room to place their first counter in. After players have placed both their counters, the treasure is shared out. Treasure is shared equally according to the number of counters in each room. For example, four counters in the room with two blocks means that each player gets half of the treasure. The first player will usually choose the room with three blocks, but after that choices can be discussed, as strategies will vary.

Be aware

- Children may not realise at first that a common denominator is essential to solving such problems.

Outcomes

- I can add and subtract related fractions.
- I can solve a set of fraction problems and record my solutions.

Challenge Plan: Year 4

E1: count in 2s, 3s, 4s, 5s, 10s, 25s, 50s; multiplication and division facts; fractions and mixed numbers; equivalent simple fractions

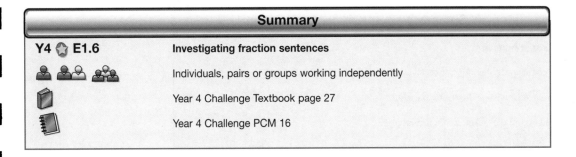

Summary

Y4 ✦ E1.6	**Investigating fraction sentences**
	Individuals, pairs or groups working independently
	Year 4 Challenge Textbook page 27
	Year 4 Challenge PCM 16

Abacus Evolve objectives

- **Y5** Use fraction notation, including mixed numbers, and the vocabulary 'numerator' and 'denominator'
- **Y5** Recognise when two simple fractions are equivalent
- **Y5** Rehearse regular and irregular polygons
- **Y5** Know the meaning of 'diagonal' of a polygon

Framework objectives

- **Y5** Express a smaller whole number as a fraction of a larger one (e.g. recognise that 5 out of 8 is $\frac{5}{8}$); find equivalent fractions (e.g. $\frac{7}{10} = \frac{14}{20}$, or $\frac{19}{10} = 1\frac{9}{10}$); relate fractions to their decimal representations
- **Y5** Identify, visualise and describe properties of rectangles, triangles, regular polygons and 3D solids; use knowledge of properties to draw 2D shapes, and identify and draw nets of 3D shapes

Teacher notes

Preparation
Photocopy PCM 16, one copy per child or pair.

Activity
Children work from Textbook page 27. They see a regular hexagon with two diagonals dividing the shape into three parts. A fraction sentence is given for this: $\frac{2}{3} + \frac{1}{6} + \frac{1}{6} = 1$. They explore drawing different diagonals on the hexagons on PCM 16 and writing matching fraction sentences. When they have exhausted these possibilities they turn to the hexagrams (stars based on hexagons) on the PCM and extend their investigation. They should end up with a collection of fraction sentences justified by the lines they have drawn to divide the shapes.

Information
Polygrams were as important to Ancient Greek mathematics as polygons. Regular polygrams join the corners of a regular polygon, making a pattern with the diagonals. Here is a polygram based on the regular octagon – an octagram.

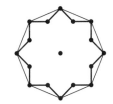

Be aware

- In this activity it is possible for children to create parts of the hexagon or hexagram that they cannot find as a fraction. This will allow children to learn that in maths some problems can be created but are too difficult to solve.

Outcomes

- I can investigate fractions within shapes.
- I can split regular polygons and polygrams into fractions and create fraction sentences.

Challenge Plan: Year 4

A2: count on/back in 1s, 10s, 100s, 1000s; numbers to 10 000; 'between' numbers; add/subtract odd/even numbers; negative numbers

Summary

Y4 ⬡ A2.1

Larger numbers

A small group working with an adult

Year 4 Challenge Textbook page 28

Six-sided dice; digit cards (optional)

Abacus Evolve objectives

- Add or subtract 1, 10, 100 or 1000 to or from any integer
- Consolidate understanding of the relationship between addition and subtraction
- Read and write numbers up to 100 000 in figures and words
- Know what each digit in a 5-digit number represents

Framework objectives

- Use knowledge of addition and subtraction facts and place value to derive sums and differences of pairs of multiples of 10, 100 or 1000

Teacher notes

Getting started

Look at Textbook page 28 with the group. Explain how the dice code works. Throw a dice. *The number it lands on matches to an addition or a subtraction*. Check that children understand the dice code on the Textbook page (throw 1 – add 100, throw 2 – subtract 1000, throw 3 – add 10 000, throw 4 – add 1000, throw 5 – subtract 10 000, throw 6 – subtract 100). Demonstrate how it works by choosing a 5-digit number from the top of the page, throwing a dice to generate an addition or subtraction, and modelling the calculation.

Ask a child to choose a 5-digit number and throw a dice. They tell the group what the number is and what the calculation is. The group work together to find the answer. Repeat until all the children have had a go.

Activity

Children work from Textbook page 28. In pairs or threes, they take turns to throw two dice and carry out the corresponding additions or subtractions on each of the nine 5-digit numbers. They then move on to throwing three dice for each number. Children can then try using one of the other three codes shown on the page, or they can invent their own code and use this.

If you have time

Children can use digit cards to create new 5-digit numbers, then repeat the activity using these.

Be aware

- Lining up the digits correctly when adding and subtracting large numbers is challenging and may need support.
- Some children may need support and modelling when applying a series of inverse operations to numbers at first.

Outcomes

- I can add and subtract large numbers.
- I can explain what each digit represents in a large number.

Supporting resources

Excel worksheets 'Addition square worksheet generator' and 'Sums square addition' are useful and can be downloaded from:
- www.primaryresources.co.uk/maths/mathsC1.htm

Look at the programs 'Number bonds' and 'Function machine' at:
- www.bgfl.org/bgfl/custom/resources_ftp/client_ftp/ks2/maths/canterbury_cross

Challenge Plan: Year 4

A2: count on/back in 1s, 10s, 100s, 1000s; numbers to 10 000;
'between' numbers; add/subtract odd/even numbers; negative numbers

Summary

Y4 ✦ A2.2

Adding sequences with Gauss

Individuals, pairs or groups working independently

Year 4 Challenge Textbook page 29

1–100 number squares

Abacus Evolve objectives

- Compare and order numbers up to 10 000
- Recognise the properties of odd and even numbers, including their sums and differences

Framework objectives

- Partition, round and order 4-digit whole numbers; use positive and negative numbers in context and position them on a number line; state inequalities using the symbols < and >, e.g. $^-3 > ^-5$, $^-1 < ^+1$
- *Add or subtract mentally pairs of two-digit whole numbers (e.g. 47 + 58, 91 − 35)*
- Identify and use patterns, relationships and properties of numbers or shapes; investigate a statement involving numbers and test it with examples

Teacher notes

Preparation
Provide some 1 to 100 number squares to give children visual cues.

Getting started
Ask children to practise adding three or four 1-digit numbers (such as 3, 4, 5, 6) as an introduction to the activity.

Activity
Children work from Textbook page 29. They read about how Gauss found a shortcut to add all the numbers from 1 to 100. They check the calculation for themselves to see if Gauss was right. Children discuss their strategies.
The textbook page sets other challenges adding consecutive numbers, consecutive odd numbers and consecutive even numbers. Finally problems are posed where the sum is known, but the consecutive numbers added are not. These are solved using division to find the central numbers in the sequence (for example 84 ÷ 7 = 12, 9 + 10 + 11 + **12** + 13 + 14 + 15 = 84).

Information
Gauss noticed that the first number (1) and the last number (100) added up to 101, and that the second number (2) and the second to last number (99) also added to 101. He realised that all the numbers could be paired up like this. He knew there were 50 pairs so he just had to multiply 101 by 50 in his head. A quick way to do this is to multiply 101 by 100 (10 100), then halving it (5050).
If you would like to demonstrate this, write one column starting with 1, 2, 3, … then a second column alongside starting with 100, 99, 98, … Add across each row and make a new column for the total. *The columns always add to 101! How many rows should there be?* (50) *What is 100 × 101?* (10 100). *Halve this to get 5050.*

Be aware

- Children are not likely to come up with Gauss's strategy on their own, but they may get there with some guidance.

Outcomes

- I can find quick ways to add up sequences of numbers.
- I can quickly add pairs of numbers.
- I can work out what consecutive numbers were added together from looking at the total.

Supporting resources

General problem-solving activities can be found at:
- nrich.maths.org/public/search.php?search=summing%20sequences&filters[ks2]=1

Challenge Plan: Year 4

A2: count on/back in 1s, 10s, 100s, 1000s; numbers to 10 000; 'between' numbers; add/subtract odd/even numbers; negative numbers

Summary

Y4 ⬡ A2.3

Estimating game

Groups working independently

Year 4 Challenge Textbook page 30

Year 4 Challenge PCM 17

Calculators; stopclock or watch

Abacus Evolve objectives

- **Y5** Make and justify estimates of large numbers
- **Y5** Estimate simple proportions such as one third, seven tenths
- **Y5** Use known number facts and place value to multiply or divide mentally
- **Y5** Multiply by 19, 21, … by multiplying by 20, … and adjusting

Framework objectives

- **Y5** Recall quickly multiplication facts up to 10 × 10 and use them to multiply pairs of multiples of 10 and 100; derive quickly corresponding division facts
- **Y5** Extend mental methods for whole-number calculations, for example to multiply a two-digit by one-digit number (e.g. 12 × 9), to multiply by 25 (e.g. 16 × 25), to subtract one near-multiple of 1000 from another (e.g. 6070 − 4097)
- **Y5** Use understanding of place value to multiply and divide whole numbers and decimals by 10, 100 or 1000

Teacher notes

Preparation
Photocopy PCM 17, one copy per child. Cut them up into individual score sheets.

Getting started
Explain to children how to play the estimating game on the Textbook page. Stress that what is needed are two estimates which capture the answer between them.

Activity
Children work from Textbook page 30. The page shows how to play an estimating game. Children take turns to be the game-master. Children have 15 seconds to estimate the answer to a multiplication or division. They must say two numbers between which they think the answer falls. Once all the children in the group have estimated, the game-master finds the answer to the multiplication or division using a calculator. If the answer falls between a child's two numbers, they stay in. The game-master then works out the player who correctly estimated the answer and has the smallest difference between their two numbers. This is the winner. The game-master ranks the other children left in, based on how large the difference between their two numbers. The group play the game several times, using the score sheets from PCM 17 to record their estimates and results.

Extra help
Children can practise estimating answers, before estimating two numbers that an answer could fall between.

If you have time
Play the game again, allowing less time for estimation.

Be aware

- When finding fractions of numbers children may require support in recognising the need to divide (for example to find $\frac{1}{5}$ of a number, divide by 5).
- It may be necessary to suggest how to round numbers up or down quickly, making multiplying easier.

Outcomes

- I can quickly estimate the answer to different problems in my head.
- I can multiply multiples of 10.
- I can estimate simple fractions of numbers.

Supporting resources

Children can practise estimating using the games at:
- www.mathopolis.com/estimate-multiplytens.php
- www.prongo.com/math/multiplication.html

Challenge Plan: Year 4

A2: count on/back in 1s, 10s, 100s, 1000s; numbers to 10 000;
'between' numbers; add/subtract odd/even numbers; negative numbers

Summary

Y4 ✪ A2.4

Six circles

A small group working with an adult

Year 4 Challenge PCM 18

Sticky notes

Abacus Evolve objectives

- Find what to add to a 2- or 3-digit number to make 100 or the next multiple of 100
- Use known number facts and place value to add two 2-digit numbers, adding the tens first
- Choose and use appropriate operations and appropriate ways of calculating (mental, mental with jottings, pencil and paper) to solve problems
- Add and subtract 2- and 3-digit multiples of 10
- Recognise and explain patterns and relationships, generalise and predict

Framework objectives

- Use knowledge of addition and subtraction facts and place value to derive sums and differences of pairs of multiples of 10, 100 or 1000
- Suggest a line of enquiry and the strategy needed to follow it; collect, organise and interpret selected information to find answers
- Report solutions to puzzles and problems, giving explanations and reasoning orally and in writing, using diagrams and symbols
- Identify and use patterns, relationships and properties of numbers or shapes; investigate a statement involving numbers and test it with examples

Teacher notes

Preparation
Photocopy PCM 18, one copy per child.

Getting started
Give each child a copy of PCM 18. Draw a large version of the magic triangle made of six circles. Use numbered sticky notes to investigate ways of placing 10, 20, 30, 40, 50 and 60 in the circles. *Calculate the total of each side. Can you make the sides all have the same total? How different can you make the totals for each side?*

Activity
Ask children to make all sides total 100, recording their solution on the PCM. *Can it be done more than one way?* When all children have completed the '100' triangle, compare solutions. Point out that they are all reflections or rotations of each other. Ask children to work out how many different looking arrangements there can be of 'the same' solution. (They match the symmetries of an equilateral triangle.) Children solve the rest of the possible totals: 90, 110 and 120. *Are there others?* (No) *Why is 90 the minimum and 120 the maximum?* (90 is the lowest total that includes 60; 120 is the highest total that includes 10.)

Give children a different set of six numbers (50, 100, 150, 200, 250, 300) to place. *What are the possible totals now?* If they solve it quickly, ask them how they did it – did they use their previous result? Move on to the six numbers 120, 150, 170, 200, 220, 250. *How many solutions are there this time? What totals are possible?*

Further extension
Investigate the numbers 10, 20, 30, …, 80, 90 in a triangle with four circles on each side.

Be aware

- Some children may need help to see patterns and apply what they did in the first problem to the second problem.
- These are open-ended questions, with more than one answer at times, so children need to be flexible and draw on each other's ideas.

Outcomes

- I can arrange numbers around a triangle to make the sides add up to different totals.
- I can rotate my diagram so it matches my partner's.
- I can add multiples of 10 in my head.
- I can use ideas from problems I have solved to help me answer other problems quickly.

Challenge Plan: Year 4

Summary

Y4 **A2.5**

Exploring arithmagons

Individuals, pairs or groups working independently

Year 4 Challenge Textbook page 31

Year 4 Challenge PCM 19

Abacus Evolve objectives

- Consolidate understanding of the relationship between addition and subtraction
- Use known number facts and place value to add two 2-digit numbers, adding the tens first
- Choose and use appropriate operations and appropriate ways of calculating (mental, mental with jottings, pencil and paper) to solve problems
- Recognise negative numbers in context
- Recognise and explain patterns and relationships, generalise and predict

Framework objectives

- Use knowledge of addition and subtraction facts and place value to derive sums and differences of pairs of multiples of 10, 100 or 1000
- Report solutions to puzzles and problems, giving explanations and reasoning orally and in writing, using diagrams and symbols
- Suggest a line of enquiry and the strategy needed to follow it; collect, organise and interpret selected information to find answers
- Identify and use patterns, relationships and properties of numbers or shapes; investigate a statement involving numbers and test it with examples

Teacher notes

Preparation
Photocopy PCM 19, one copy per child.

Activity
Children work from Textbook page 31. They read about arithmagons, then complete the first four arithmagons on PCM 19. Children then explore solutions to more challenging problems using blank arithmagons. This gives children a basis for exploring further examples and to invent fresh problems themselves.

Information
This activity adds breadth to children's problem solving strategies and reasoning, developing their problem posing abilities further.

Be aware

- Some initial support using a number line may be required with negative number arithmagons.
- Thinking backwards through calculations may not be obvious to some children (for example if the two numbers total 120 and one of the numbers is 25, what is the other?).
- Discussion and thinking about strategies will be beneficial. Trial and improvement and becoming systematic should be encouraged.

Outcomes

- I can add and subtract 2- and 3-digit numbers in my head and using paper.
- I can spot patterns and work out rules to help me find answers more quickly.
- I can work out what two numbers were added when I know the total.
- I can suggest ways of working things out and then carry them through systematically.

Supporting resources

A spreadsheet which generates arithmagons is at:
- http://www.lgfl.net/lgfl/leas/enfield/schools/southgate/accounts/staff/dwhitfield/web/pages/teacher_resources_contents.html#arithmagons

Challenge Plan: Year 4

A2: count on/back in 1s, 10s, 100s, 1000s; numbers to 10 000; 'between' numbers; add/subtract odd/even numbers; negative numbers

Summary

Y4 ⭐ A2.6   **Positive and negative number loops**

Groups working independently

Year 4 Challenge Textbook page 32

Year 4 Challenge PCM 20

Thin card; blank cards

Abacus Evolve objectives

- **Y5** Order a given set of positive and negative numbers
- **Y5** Use known number facts and place value to multiply or divide mentally

Framework objectives

- **Y5** Count from any given number in whole-number and decimal steps, extending beyond zero when counting backwards; relate the numbers to their position on a number line

Teacher notes

Preparation
Photocopy PCM 20 onto thin card. Cut out the playing cards. If more than four children are playing, two sets may be needed.
A set of blank cards will be needed for the Extra activity.

Getting started
Children look at the ⁻50 to ⁺50 number line on Textbook page 32. They warm up using the questions on the Textbook page, referring to the number line as the key image. When they are confident with these they move on to playing the game.

Activity
Children work from Textbook page 32. They use the linking cards from PCM 20. First they check that the additions and subtractions on the four sets are correct and form a loop. They then play the game with a full pack of 24 cards, with up to six cards per player. Any residual cards are used as a pick-up pack when a player cannot go. Children take turns and play or pass if they cannot play a card that follows the one on the table.

Be aware

- It can be confusing adding and subtracting positive and negative numbers, so use a number line to support children's thinking. Moving from doing a calculation on a number line to doing it in their heads is a learning step, not an automatic process.

Outcomes

- I can use a number line to help me add and subtract positive and negative numbers.
- I can add and subtract positive and negative numbers in my head.

Supporting resources

Games involving positive and negative numbers can be found at:
- nrich.maths.org/public/monthindex.php?year=2008&month=01&choice=3&showfulltier=yes&submit=GO
- www.education-world.com/a_tsl/archives/03-1/lesson001

Sequences of numbers, positive and negative, can be investigated using the 'Four digit sequencer' on:
- www.crickweb.co.uk/ks2numeracy

Challenge Plan: Year 4

B2: doubles and halves up to 50; doubles and halves of multiples of 10 and 100; classifying 2D shapes; names and nets of 3D shapes

Summary

Y4 ⭐ B2.1

Halving and doubling shapes

A small group working with an adult

Year 4 Challenge Textbook page 33

Year 4 Challenge PCM 21

2 cm square dotted paper; rulers; scissors; sticky tape

Abacus Evolve objectives

- **Y5** Rehearse the names and properties of common 2D shapes
- **Y5** Know the meaning of 'diagonal' of a polygon

Framework objectives

- **Y5** Identify, visualise and describe properties of rectangles, triangles, regular polygons and 3D solids; use knowledge of properties to draw 2D shapes, and to identify and draw nets of 3D shapes
- **Y5** Explore patterns, properties and relationships and propose a general statement involving numbers or shapes; identify examples for which the statement is true or false

Teacher notes

Preparation
Photocopy PCM 21, one copy per child. Provide 2 cm square dot grid paper.

Activity
- Discuss how to find halving lines of symmetrical shapes. (They are straight lines which go through the centre of the shape and split the shape into two equal halves). Demonstrate how to find the centre of different symmetrical shapes by drawing both diagonals. Then use the centre point to draw halving lines.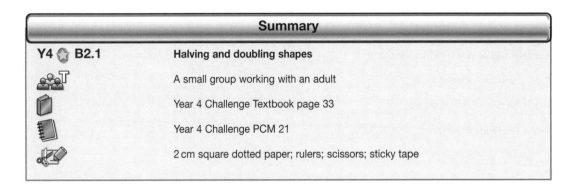
- Show how to make a chain of shapes, starting with a rectangle. Find the centre of the shape, halve it, then double that shape to produce a new shape. Find a new halving line and repeat.

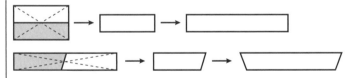

- Children work from Textbook page 33. They cut out the shapes on PCM 21 and investigate halving and doubling them.
- Children then have a go at creating longer chains starting with one of the shapes on PCM 21. This time encourage children to draw the shapes on dotted paper, rather than cutting them out. *How many steps can you do without repeating a shape?* Children discuss and share strategies and examples. Strategies should include ideas of symmetry and the fact that the area of each doubled shape is the same.

Extra help
Draw 4 × 4 squares on square dot or squared paper. Children who have not previously explored halving shapes can try halving the squares in as many different ways as they can find.

If you have time
Children draw the first and last shapes from a chain and swap them within the group. *What are the missing shapes in the chain? What is happening to the areas of the new shapes in the chains?* (The area of each doubled shape is always the same). *Can this be used to find the areas of difficult shapes?* (Some difficult shapes can be halved and doubled to change them into rectangles. It is easier to find the area of a rectangle.)

Be aware

- Some children may need support when they are asked to visualise and draw the shapes rather than cutting them out.
- Children should understand the concept of area but will not need to calculate it.

Outcomes

- I can draw diagonals to find the centre of symmetrical shapes.
- I can halve a symmetrical shape by drawing a straight line through its centre.
- I can double shapes to find new symmetrical shapes.

Supporting resources

Children can explore making symmetrical shapes using 'Reflecting squarely':
- nrich.maths.org/public/viewer.php?obj_id=1840

Challenge Plan: Year 4

B2: doubles and halves up to 50; doubles and halves of multiples of 10 and 100; classifying 2D shapes; names and nets of 3D shapes

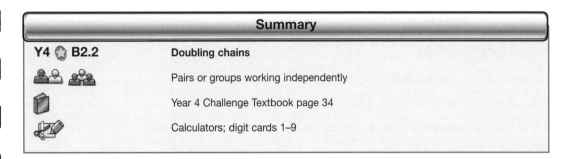

Summary

Y4 ⭐ B2.2

Doubling chains

Pairs or groups working independently

Year 4 Challenge Textbook page 34

Calculators; digit cards 1–9

Abacus Evolve objectives

- Double or halve 2-digit numbers by doubling or halving the tens first
- Derive doubles of integers up to 50 and the corresponding halves
- Use known number facts and place value to multiply or divide mentally

Framework objectives

- Identify the doubles of 2-digit numbers; use these to calculate doubles of multiples of 10 and 100 and derive the corresponding halves

Teacher notes

Getting started
Briefly run through mental methods for doubling. Review how to check doubling by halving using a calculator (use the buttons ÷, 2 and =). Give each pair a set of digit cards 1–9.

Activity
Children work from Textbook page 34. They look at a doubling chain created by starting with the number 1 and doubling repeatedly until a 6-digit number is reached.
Children then practise doubling 1-digit numbers four times. They start a doubling chain for each of the numbers 1 to 9, then they consider which numbers appear in more than one sequence (even numbers).

Children then play a doubling game in pairs or groups. Digit cards 1–9 are shuffled and placed face down in a pile. Each child takes a card without showing it. They double this number mentally until they reach a 6-digit number. Children record the sequence. They then check their answers by halving with a calculator and correct any errors. Children swap their 6-digit numbers with another child and use halving to find the original 1-digit number. Children should not use a calculator for this part.

Extra help
Encourage children to have a go with using mental methods to double, then check their answers by halving with a calculator. Children should not need to resort to using a calculator throughout.

If you have time
Children can try to continue doubling up to 7-digit numbers and play the game again.

Be aware

- Some children may require more support when doubling and halving larger numbers mentally.
- Children can double by adding the number to itself or by multiplying by 2. Make sure they can distinguish between these two techniques and are confident with the one they have chosen to use.

Outcomes

- I can double and halve numbers with up to six digits.
- I can work out which small number has been repeatedly doubled by repeatedly halving a large number.
- I can check my working by using a calculator.

Supporting resources

There are many doubling and halving games at:
- www.primaryresources.co.uk/maths/mathsC4.htm

Challenge Plan: Year 4

B2: doubles and halves up to 50; doubles and halves of multiples of 10 and 100; classifying 2D shapes; names and nets of 3D shapes

Summary

Y4 ⬟ B2.3

Steps to triangular numbers

Individuals, pairs or groups working independently

Year 4 Challenge Textbook page 35

Linking cubes; 2 cm square dotted paper; 100-squares

Abacus Evolve objectives

- Identify near doubles using known doubles
- Recognise and explain patterns and relationships, generalise and predict
- Make and investigate a general statement about familiar numbers or shapes by finding examples that satisfy it (number)

Framework objectives

- Identify the doubles of 2-digit numbers; use to calculate doubles of multiples of 10 and 100 and derive the corresponding halves
- Identify and use patterns, relationships and properties of numbers or shapes; investigate a statement involving numbers and test it with examples
- Report solutions to puzzles and problems, giving explanations and reasoning orally and in writing, using diagrams and symbols

Teacher notes

Getting started
Make the three sets of steps on Textbook page 35 to demonstrate how the number of cubes increases each time. Draw children's attention to how many cubes you are using to make each set of steps.
Provide 10 linking cubes, 2 cm square dotted paper and a 100-square for each child.

Activity
Children work from Textbook page 35. They make sets of steps from cubes to become acquainted with the notion of triangular numbers. They draw the sequence of steps increasing in size to generate the triangular numbers up to 105. They mark these numbers on a 100-square, then explore the properties of the sequence. They should discover that triangular numbers are formed by adding 1, 2, 3, 4, … and so on, each time.

Further extension
Children can explore square numbers in this way, using steps that go up and down. They use a different colour to shade the square numbers on their 100-square.
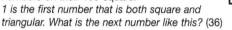
1 is the first number that is both square and triangular. What is the next number like this? (36)
Can you add any two triangular numbers that are not next to each other and get a square number? When is the difference of two square numbers a triangular number? Can you add two square numbers and get another square number?

Information
The first 15 triangular numbers are: 1, 3, 6, 10, 15, 21, 28, 36, 45, 55, 66, 78, 91, 105, 120.

Be aware

- Children will need to focus on the visual element of this activity. You may need to check that they are drawing their steps accurately so that they can understand the concept of triangular numbers.

Outcomes

- I can create a sequence of numbers by recording a pattern of steps.
- I can investigate a sequence and find patterns.
- I can recognise triangular numbers.

Challenge Plan: Year 4

B2: doubles and halves up to 50; doubles and halves of multiples of 10 and 100; classifying 2D shapes; names and nets of 3D shapes

Summary

Y4 ✿ B2.4	**Understanding tetrahedra**
	A small group working with an adult
	Year 4 Challenge PCM 22
	Thin card; scissors; A4 paper in four colours; sticky tape

Abacus Evolve objectives

- Recognise equilateral and isosceles triangles
- Begin to use the terms 'polyhedron' and 'tetrahedron'
- Describe and visualise 3D shapes
- Visualise 3D shapes from 2D drawings and identify simple nets of solid shapes

Framework objectives

- Draw polygons and classify them by identifying their properties, including their line symmetry
- Visualise 3D objects from 2D drawings; make nets of common solids
- Use and reflect on some ground rules for dialogue (e.g. making structured, extended contributions, speaking audibly, making meaning explicit and listening actively)

Teacher notes

Preparation
Photocopy PCM 22, one copy per child (onto thin card if possible). Make and cut out a large copy of each these two nets, on thin card.

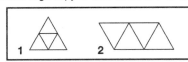

Cut out four equilateral triangles from different-coloured paper and use them to make four 'trigulls' like this:

1. Fold the equilateral triangle into four small equilateral triangles.

2. Cut down the centre of the three outer triangles.

3. Fold back half of each outer triangle to make three wings.

'Trigulls' can be joined to make regular polyhedra by slotting the wings into adjoining 'trigulls'. Slot your 'trigulls' together to make a regular tetrahedron (triangle-based pyramid).

Activity
A polyhedron is a 3D shape made from polygons. A tetrahedron is the simplest polyhedron.
Show children your tetrahedron and discuss its properties: four equilateral triangle faces, four vertices, six edges.
Show the first net. *Will this net fold into a regular tetrahedron?* (Yes).
Show the second net. *Will this net fold into a regular tetrahedron?* (No). Encourage children to visualise the answer first, then fold the net to find out.
Children cut out the four copies of the seven types of triangle. They explore making tetrahedron nets with combinations of four triangles. Bring to their notice that sides of triangles must match if they are to be joined. Remind them that the word *tetrahedron* simply means *four faced*. A tetrahedron does not have to be made of equilateral triangles. For example this is an effective tetrahedron net that children might make:

Extra help
Suggest that children start with an equilateral triangle as the base and explore using three isosceles triangles for the other three faces.

If you have time
Children can explore making and combining 'trigulls' to create more polyhedra.

Information
Polyhedra with equilateral triangle faces include the three regular polyhedra: tetrahedron, octahedron and icosahedron.

Be aware

- Children may not be adept at folding paper. Give support where necessary.

Outcomes

- I know the properties of tetrahedra.
- I can visualise a 3D shape from its net.
- I can test my ideas by making 3D shapes from nets.

Supporting resources

To manipulate some simple nets go to 'Cut-outs, Nets' here:
- http://www.fi.uu.nl/wisweb/en/

Challenge Plan: Year 4

B2: doubles and halves up to 50; doubles and halves of multiples of 10 and 100; classifying 2D shapes; names and nets of 3D shapes

Summary

Y4 ⬡ B2.5

Properties of polyhedra

Individuals, pairs or groups working independently

Year 4 Challenge Textbook page 36

Year 4 Challenge PCMs 23 and 24

Simple polyhedra; polygons; strong glue (optional)

Abacus Evolve objectives

- Begin to use the terms 'polyhedron' and 'tetrahedron'
- Describe and visualise 3D shapes
- Rehearse the names of common 3D shapes
- Recognise and explain patterns and relationships, generalise and predict
- Make and investigate a general statement about familiar numbers or shapes by finding examples that satisfy it (shape)

Framework objectives

- Visualise 3D objects from 2D drawings; make nets of common solids
- Identify and use patterns, relationships and properties of numbers or shapes; investigate a statement involving numbers and test it with examples

Teacher notes

Preparation
Photocopy PCMs 23 and 24, one copy of each per pair.

Getting started
Introduce the terms polyhedron and polyhedra (3D shapes). Show examples of prisms and pyramids and discuss the shapes.
(A tetrahedron is the same as a triangular pyramid.)
Give children plenty of polygons to use in their explorations. If you are happy for children to glue these polygons together, provide them with strong glue.

Activity
Children work from Textbook page 36. They look at a table showing the numbers of triangles and squares that make up a triangular prism, a square pyramid and a tetrahedron.
Children then look at two tables on PCM 23, one showing five prisms and the second showing five pyramids. Children use polygons to investigate the numbers of vertices, edges and faces of each prism/pyramid. They use this information to complete the two tables. They discuss any patterns they notice.
Children then complete the table on PCM 24 and discuss any patterns they can see in the table.

Further extension
Place a pyramid onto a mirror. *What shape do the pyramid and its mirror image make?* (Two pyramids symmetrically placed base-to-base are called a dipyramid.)
Children can try with other polyhedra and see what shapes they make. Discuss the properties of the shapes. Introduce the idea of symmetry – the mirror is a plane of symmetry.

Be aware

- Try to show children real examples of the polyhedra. 2D views of a shape can be deceptive and children may not be able to visualise what is not visible in the picture.

Outcomes

- I can investigate the properties of a range of polyhedra.
- I know the names polyhedron and tetrahedron.
- I can visualise 3D shapes.

Supporting resources

Resources for exploring polyhedra, including images, can be found at:
- www.mathsisfun.com/platonic_solids

Challenge Plan: Year 4

B2: doubles and halves up to 50; doubles and halves of multiples of 10 and 100; classifying 2D shapes; names and nets of 3D shapes

Summary

Y4 ⭐ B2.6

Pentominoes and cube nets

Pairs or groups working independently

Year 4 Challenge Textbook page 37

Square dot grid paper; scissors; sticky tape

Abacus Evolve objectives

- **Y5** Visualise 3D shapes from 2D drawings and identify different nets of 3D shapes
- **Y5** Understand the terms 'reflective symmetry' and 'axis of symmetry'
- **Y5** Recognise where a shape will be after reflection in a mirror line parallel to one side

Framework objectives

- **Y5** Identify, visualise and describe properties of rectangles, triangles, regular polygons and 3D solids; use knowledge of properties to draw 2D shapes, and to identify and draw nets of 3D shapes
- **Y5** Complete patterns with up to two lines of symmetry; draw the position of a shape after a reflection or translation
- **Y5** Plan and pursue an enquiry; present evidence by collecting, organising and interpreting information; suggest extensions to the enquiry
- **Y5** Understand the process of decision making

Teacher notes

Getting started
Explain that a pentomino is a shape made from five squares joined together.

Activity
Children work from Textbook page 37. Pentominoes are defined and an example is given. Children are reminded that rotating, reflecting or flipping the shape do not produce a 'new' pentomino.
Children search systematically for all the different pentominoes. (There are 12.) A good strategy is to start by drawing the five tetrominoes and adding an extra square. They draw the pentominoes on square dot grid paper. Children then discuss whether they are sure they have found them all.
Children then consider the 12 pentominoes as potential nets for an open cube (a box without a lid). They decide which will work as open cube nets, then make the open cubes.
They then investigate adding an extra square to pentominoes to make closed cube nets.

Further extension
Children share out the 12 pentominoes with a partner, so each child has six. In secret they fit their pentominoes together to make a shape. They draw round its outline and give the outline to their partner. Can children work out how to fit the six pentominoes into the shape outline?

If you have time
Children can investigate possible nets for a regular octahedron (made from eight equilateral triangles). There are 11 possible nets. They compare the symmetries of these with the closed cube nets (they match exactly).

Information
Half of the pentominoes have line symmetry and half do not.

Be aware

- Visualising nets as 3D shapes is challenging so children should be encouraged to make them practically and share ideas about them.

Outcomes

- I can investigate systematically.
- I can visualise folding nets into 3D shapes.
- I can recognise reflections and rotations of pentominoes.

Supporting resources

Resources for nets can be found at:
- www.primaryresources.co.uk/maths/mathsE3.htm

C2: measuring capacity; reading simple timetables; perimeter and area; constructing and interpreting bar graphs

Summary

Y4 ☆ C2.1

Capacity puzzles

A small group working with an adult

Year 4 Challenge Textbook page 38

A set of empty plastic bottles; water

Abacus Evolve objectives

- Use, read and write standard metric units of capacity: l, ml
- Rehearse the relationship between litres and millilitres

Framework objectives

- *Choose and use standard metric units and their abbreviations when estimating, measuring and recording length, weight and capacity; know the meaning of 'kilo', 'centi' and 'milli' and, where appropriate, use decimal notation to record measurements (e.g. 1·3 m or 0·6 kg)*
- *Solve one-step and two-step problems involving numbers, money or measures, including time; choose and carry out appropriate calculations, using calculator methods where appropriate*
- *Respond appropriately to the contributions of others in the light of alternative viewpoints*

Teacher notes

Preparation
Collect a set of empty plastic bottles, with capacities of 50 cl, 75 cl, 1 litre, 1·5 litres and 2 litres. There should be no marks on the bottles. Make sure you are near a tap.

Activity
- *By filling, pouring and emptying only, we will work out how to end up with exactly 50 cl left in one of these bottles. How many centilitres are in 2 litres?* (200) Model one example with a 2 litre bottle and a 75 cl bottle: Fill the 2 litre bottle. Pour 75 cl of water into the 75 cl bottle. Empty the 75 cl bottle. Pour another 75 cl into the 75 cl bottle. There should now be 50 cl left in the 2 litre bottle. Check by pouring the water into the 50 cl bottle. *How many steps did we take to solve the problem?* Agree that it took four steps.
- Challenge children to use the 1 litre bottle and the 1·5 litre bottle to end up with exactly 50 cl of water. Allow them time to discuss as a group, agree on a plan, and then try to solve the problem. They can check using the 50 cl bottle. *How many steps did you take? Could you do it in fewer steps?*
- Children work from Textbook page 38. They encounter increasingly difficult capacity problems, based on the processes they have just tried out. As they proceed through, discuss any general strategies they are using.

Extra help
Show vertical number lines from zero to the capacity of each bottle and beyond. By looking at pairs or threes that represent the capacities in the puzzle, children can relate understanding of numbers and adding and subtracting to finding solutions.

Further extension
Children make the capacity cards from the Extra activity on the Textbook page. They each pick three cards and apply strategies they have developed to find all possible capacities that could be made with their three bottles.

Be aware

- Depending upon their preferred learning styles, children may need more practical time in order to develop their own strategies.

Outcomes

- I can solve logic puzzles about capacities in litres and centilitres.
- I understand that 100 centilitres make 1 litre.

Supporting resources

Interactive capacity puzzles can be found at:
- http://www.tradingfleet.com/stem2000/measure1.swf

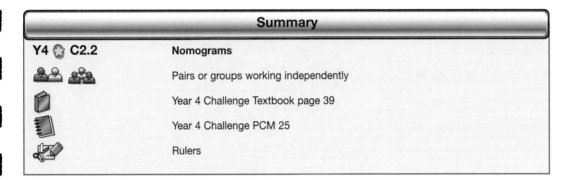

Challenge Plan: Year 4

C2: measuring capacity; reading simple timetables; perimeter and area; constructing and interpreting bar graphs

Summary

Y4 ⭐ C2.2

Nomograms

Pairs or groups working independently

Year 4 Challenge Textbook page 39

Year 4 Challenge PCM 25

Rulers

Abacus Evolve objectives

- Begin to use imperial units of capacity: pints
- Consolidate understanding of the relationship between addition and subtraction
- Record estimates and readings from capacity scales

Framework objectives

- *Choose and use standard metric units and their abbreviations when estimating, measuring and recording length, weight and capacity; know the meaning of 'kilo', 'centi' and 'milli' and, where appropriate, use decimal notation to record measurements (e.g. 1·3 m or 0·6 kg)*
- *Interpret intervals and divisions on partially numbered scales and record readings accurately, where appropriate to the nearest tenth of a unit*

Teacher notes

Preparation
Photocopy PCM 25, one copy per individual, pair or group. Familiarise yourself with the concept of a nomogram.

Getting started
Together read through the definition of a nomogram on the Textbook page. Check that children understand this and can use the capacity conversion nomogram on the PCM.

Activity
Children work from Textbook page 39. They learn about nomograms, then look at the litres–pints nomogram on PCM 25. They need to work out how to use the nomogram to answer conversion questions: lay a ruler across the two lines, so that the line goes through the starting point (i.e. the point where the example dotted line starts) and the value that they wish to convert.
Children are then introduced to an addition nomogram with three parallel lines. This nomogram can also be used for subtraction. Children use the nomogram to find answers to additions and subtractions.

Extra help
If children are finding the scales difficult to interpret, relate one scale to their experiences of number lines and counting sticks. Build up children's confidence that scale works by counting up and down with the children.

Information
Nomograms are no longer used in schools, but they remain valuable tools for calculation in a variety of different fields. Most nomograms are much more complex than those used here.

Be aware

- It may take children some time to recognise the scale in these nomograms but once they have they should find it reasonably straightforward to use the nomograms to answer questions.

Outcomes

- I know about nomograms.
- I can use a nomogram to convert between pints and litres.

Summary

Y4 ⭐ **C2.3**

Timetables

Individuals, pairs or groups working independently

Year 4 Challenge Textbook page 40

Year 4 Challenge PCM 26

Abacus Evolve objectives

- **Y5** Use timetables
- **Y5** Read the time on a 24-hour digital clock and use 24-hour clock notation

Framework objectives

- **Y5** Read timetables and time using 24-hour clock notation; use a calendar to calculate time intervals
- **Y5** Understand the process of decision making

Teacher notes

Getting started
Check that children are able to work with and understand 24-hour clock notation.

Activity
Children work from Textbook page 40. They look at the train timetable on PCM 26 and answer questions about it. The timetable uses the 24-hour clock.
Children then move on to look at the flight details of an airline on the PCM. They answer questions about flight times and plan journeys for two people.

If you have time
Children can look on the internet for actual flights from their nearest large airport. They can plan and time some flights and two-stage journeys.

Be aware

- Children who do not have personal experience of trains and air travel may need more support. It may be helpful to pair them with those who have more experience in this area.

Outcomes

- I can read timetables and flight details and use this information.
- I can read 24-hour clock times and work out the lengths of journeys.

Summary

Y4 ⬠ C2.4

Perimeter and area

A small group working with an adult

Year 4 Challenge PCM 27

Strips of paper; 1 cm square dot paper; 1 cm triangle dot paper

Abacus Evolve objectives

- **Y5** Understand, measure and calculate perimeters of rectangles
- **Y5** Understand, measure and calculate perimeters of regular polygons
- **Y5** Understand area measured in square centimetres

Framework objectives

- **Y5** *Draw and measure lines to the nearest millimetre; measure and calculate the perimeter of regular and irregular polygons; use the formula for the area of a rectangle to calculate its area*
- **Y5** Represent a puzzle or problem by identifying and recording the calculations needed to solve it; find possible solutions and confirm them in the context of the problem

Teacher notes

Preparation
Cut strips of paper from A4 sheets, at least two per child.

Activity
- Write *Perimeter = 14 cm* and *Area = 12 cm². I measured a rectangle. What are the lengths of the rectangle's sides? Use these two facts to answer the question.* Children work it out, write it down secretly and show you.
- Give children square dot paper and ask them to make their own rectangle problem, by drawing a rectangle and writing down its perimeter and its area on a strip of paper.
- The group share their rectangle problems and try to solve them together. At an appropriate point, discuss their strategies. How are they approaching these problems? Children should find a general strategy or strategies for solving this type of problem.
- Children complete the first section on PCM 27 to try out their strategies and check understanding.
- Draw this symmetrical hexagon, on plain paper.
- Show children the hexagon. Ask for suggestions as to how to find its perimeter, if you know two adjacent side lengths. (3 × the shorter length + 3 × the longer length.) Children calculate the perimeter.
- Children complete the second section on PCM 27. They apply their earlier strategies to find the lengths of the sides of symmetrical hexagons.

1 cm
3 cm

Extra help
To support the general strategies, provide four thin strips of card, two of one length and two of another. Children join these using split pins to make closed shapes. They can make a rectangle and a kite. Undo one pin and stretch the strips in a line to show that the perimeter was always two long strips and two short strips.

Further extension
Children find the areas of the shapes at the bottom of the PCM, using the line of symmetry that splits them into two identical triangles. (Shape 1 – 20 cm²; shape 2 – 84 cm²; shape 3 – 15 cm².) Remind children that the area of a triangle is always half the area of the rectangle surrounding it. Ask children to explain their strategy.

Be aware

- Children may think squares are the only units for measuring area. Show that different units, such as equilateral triangles on dot paper, can be used.

Outcomes

- I can solve problems with areas and perimeters.
- I can create similar problems of my own.

Summary

Y4 ⬡ C2.5	**Side lengths and perimeters**
👤 👥 👥👥	Individuals, pairs or groups working independently
📖	Year 4 Challenge Textbook page 41
✂️🖊️	1 cm square dot paper; 1 cm triangle dot paper; rulers; pairs of compasses

Abacus Evolve objectives

- Begin to understand the term 'perimeter'
- Understand the difference between area and perimeter
- Measure the perimeter of rectangles and other simple shapes
- Recognise and explain patterns and relationships, generalise and predict

Framework objectives

- Draw rectangles and measure and calculate their perimeters; find the area of rectilinear shapes drawn on a square grid by counting squares
- Identify and use patterns, relationships and properties of numbers or shapes; investigate a statement involving numbers and test it with examples

Teacher notes

Getting started
Run through the concepts of perimeter and area.

Activity
Children work from Textbook page 41. They draw a range of rectangles on square dot paper, that all have the perimeter 30 cm. They then explore the side lengths and the areas of these rectangles and identify the rectangles with the largest and smallest areas.
Children draw another rectangle with a perimeter of 30 cm. They find its area. They then investigate how they can change the shape, keeping the perimeter at 30 cm. They can do this by 'inverting' corners of the shape. The perimeter remains the same, but the area changes. Children draw each new shape that they find, and record the area. They explore how many different areas they can make from the same starting shape. For example a 2×13 cm rectangle has 13 possible different areas from 26 cm^2 to 14 cm^2.

26 cm^2

25 cm^2

24 cm^2

Children then compare their results as a group, and discuss what they notice.

If you have time
Using square dot paper children can consider the perimeters and areas of 'pixellated' shapes, made from edges of squares with 2 cm sides.

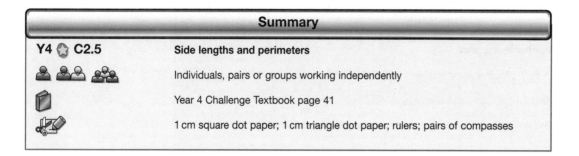

Be aware

- With triangles, children may assume that any three side lengths totalling 30 will work. However not all of these triangles can be constructed. They should be encouraged to explore which triangles work and which do not.

Outcomes

- I can find lots of possibilities and recognise how they all fit into a pattern.
- I can find a range of shapes with the same perimeter but different areas.
- I can choose an option and investigate it.

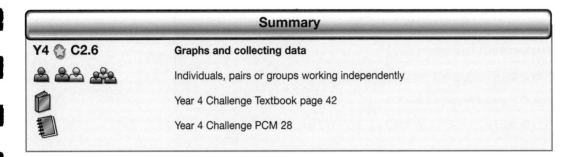

Summary

Y4 ⬡ C2.6	**Graphs and collecting data**
	Individuals, pairs or groups working independently
	Year 4 Challenge Textbook page 42
	Year 4 Challenge PCM 28

Abacus Evolve objectives

- Represent data in frequency tables
- Interpret tally charts and frequency tables
- Construct and interpret bar graphs with intervals labelled in 2s, 5s, 10s or 20s

Framework objectives

- *Answer a question by identifying what data to collect; organise, present, analyse and interpret the data in tables, diagrams, tally charts, pictograms and bar charts, using ICT where appropriate*
- Use and reflect on some ground rules for dialogue (e.g. making structured, extended contributions, speaking audibly, making meaning explicit and listening actively)

Teacher notes

Getting started
Check that children are able to understand and use simple frequency tables and bar graphs.

Activity
Children work from Textbook page 42. They start by discussing the types of question that might lead to collecting data. They are told that four children have collected data to answer a question. The raw data is provided on PCM 28 but children are not told what the question is. They speculate what the question might have been. They organise the data in a table of their design, then present it in a chart or graph of their choice. Children then come together to decide what can be discovered from the data and their graphs.

If you have time
Children collect and present their own data. They challenge other children to decide what question they were trying to answer with their data and what the data shows.

Be aware

- Getting to grips with the data-handling process takes time, so children may only begin to grasp the cycle in this lesson.

Outcomes

- I understand how to collect data to answer questions.
- I can organise data in a table and a chart or graph, then use it to find answers.

D2: adding by partitioning; subtracting 2- and 3-digit numbers; adding and subtracting near multiples of 10; adding HTU

Summary

Y4 ⭐ D2.1

Number targets

A small group working with an adult

Year 4 Challenge Textbook page 43

Digit cards 0–9

Abacus Evolve objectives

- **Y5** Develop further the relationship between addition and subtraction
- **Y5** Add two integers less than 10 000 using informal written methods
- **Y5** Add more than two integers less than 10 000

Framework objectives

- **Y5** *Use efficient written methods to add and subtract whole numbers and decimals with up to two places*
- **Y5** Solve one-step and two-step problems involving whole numbers and decimals and all four operations, choosing and using appropriate calculation strategies, including calculator use

Teacher notes

Activity

- Show three sets of digit cards 0–9. Choose the same six cards from each set and discard the other four. Arrange the cards to make three additions. Children work together to find the three totals. Point out that if we only knew the three totals we could try to work out which six digit cards were used.
- Children work from Textbook page 43. They work out which additions have been made using the digits cards listed to produce given totals.
- Children then play the game on the second half of the Textbook page. Run through the rules together. Each child starts with the digit cards 0, 2, 4, 6, 7 and 9. They make three additions with these cards and see how close they can get to the three targets:
  – Target 1: Add two 3-digit numbers. Get as close to 1000 as you can.
  – Target 2: Add two 3-digit numbers. Get as close to 900 as you can.
  – Target 3: Add three 2-digit numbers. Get as close to 180 as you can.
- Children find the difference between each total and the target. They add the differences to find their score. The child with the lowest score wins.
- Children should realise that some digits can be swapped without affecting the totals, as long as they are within the same place value, e.g. 670 + 429 = 1099, 629 + 470 = 1099, 679 + 420 = 1099, etc.

Extra help

Children can work together with one set of six digit cards. They familiarise themselves with the process by exploring different arrangements of digits and discussing the totals that are generated.

If you have time

Children can take six cards and make three additions. They give their set of six digit cards and the three totals to a partner. Their partner finds the three additions that have been made. For example 0, 2, 4, 6, 7 and 9, with targets of 1612, 676 and 136.

Be aware

- Children may try to deal with each calculation as a separate problem, and may find it quite challenging to work across three calculations together.

Outcomes

- I can work out what numbers to add to make a given total.
- I can use place value to help me make additions that are close to a target total.

Challenge Plan: Year 4

D2: adding by partitioning; subtracting 2- and 3-digit numbers; adding and subtracting near multiples of 10; adding HTU

Summary

Y4 ☆ D2.2

Palindromes

Pairs or groups working independently

Year 4 Challenge Textbook page 44

Year 4 Challenge PCM 29

Coloured pencils; calculators (optional)

Abacus Evolve objectives

- Partition 2-digit numbers into T and U (revise)
- Use known number facts and place value to add two 2-digit numbers, adding the tens first
- Add HTU + TU, HTU + HTU using informal written methods
- Recognise and explain patterns and relationships, generalise and predict

Framework objectives

- *Add or subtract mentally pairs of two-digit whole numbers (e.g. 47 + 58, 91 − 35)*
- Refine and use efficient written methods to add and subtract 2- and 3-digit whole numbers and £·p
- Identify and use patterns, relationships and properties of numbers or shapes; investigate a statement involving numbers and test it with examples
- Understand different ways to take the lead and support others in a group

Teacher notes

Preparation
Photocopy PCM 29, one copy per pair or group.

Getting started
Discuss palindromic words (e.g. dad) and numbers (e.g. 181). Make links with the idea of reflective symmetry.

Activity
Children work from Textbook page 44. They find the numbers on PCM 29 that are already palindromes and colour these in. They should be able to identify that these are multiples of 11.
Children then look at the rest of the numbers on the PCM and work out how many steps it takes to turn each of them into a palindrome. They do this by reversing the number and adding it to itself, e.g. 37 + 73 = 110. If this number is not a palindrome they repeat the step, e.g. 110 + 011 = 121. Children colour the numbers on the PCM, using a different colour for numbers that generate a palindrome after one addition, two additions, three additions and more than three additions. Children leave any numbers that go over 1000.

Further extension
Children explore the numbers that go over 1000. They use a calculator to turn one of these numbers into a palindrome and write down each number in the chain. Does it ever make a palindrome?

Information
There are six pairs of numbers that go over 1000 (59, 95; 68, 86; 69, 96; 78, 87; 79, 97 and 89, 98). The first five pairs can be made into palindromes. The last pair continues on.

Be aware

- Some children will expect patterns to be completely consistent, and may find it confusing that the ×11 table in the number square does not seem to be so.

Outcomes

- I can follow steps to find palindrome numbers.
- I can share information about palindrome numbers to find patterns.

Supporting resources

There are some more interesting facts about palindrome numbers here:
- http://www.madras.fife.sch.uk/maths/amazingnofacts/fact044.html

D2: adding by partitioning; subtracting 2- and 3-digit numbers; adding and subtracting near multiples of 10; adding HTU

Summary

Y4 ⭐ D2.3

Subtraction matching game

Individuals, pairs or groups working independently

Year 4 Challenge Textbook page 45

Year 4 Challenge PCM 30

Abacus Evolve objectives

- Understand the principles (not the names) of the commutative and associative laws as they apply or not to addition and subtraction
- Choose and use appropriate operations and appropriate ways of calculating (mental, mental with jottings, pencil and paper) to solve problems
- Subtract amounts of money, e.g. £8·40 − £3·76, using standard written method of decomposition

Framework objectives

- *Add or subtract mentally pairs of two-digit whole numbers (e.g. 47 + 58, 91 − 35)*
- Refine and use efficient written methods to add and subtract 2- and 3-digit whole numbers and £·p
- Solve one-step and two-step problems involving numbers, money or measures, including time; choose and carry out appropriate calculations, using calculator methods where appropriate

Teacher notes

Preparation
Photocopy PCM 30, one copy per child or pair. Cut up the cards.

Getting started
Read through the first question on the Textbook page together. Check that children understand how to find the answer.
Give each child or pair the three sets of cards, plus a set of blank cards.

Activity
Children work from Textbook page 45. They match the sets of cards from the PCM to make subtractions, e.g. £6·32 − £1·51 = £4·81. Children should work systematically and record their subtractions as number sentences.
Children then make their own subtraction matching game by pairing up the cards from Sets 1 and 2 in different ways and writing the new totals on blank cards. They swap their cards with a partner and put each other's cards into sets of three.

Extra help
Children can use empty number lines to support them in working out the subtractions.

Be aware

- Children will find that there are different solutions to parts of the matching problem, but not to the whole problem. They may encounter 'dead ends' if they pursue an incorrect combination of cards and may need help in overcoming these.

Outcomes

- I can subtract amounts of money.
- I can keep a clear record of a set of calculations.

Challenge Plan: Year 4

D2: adding by partitioning; subtracting 2- and 3-digit numbers; adding and subtracting near multiples of 10; adding HTU

Summary

Y4 ⭐ D2.4

Missing-number subtractions

A small group working with an adult

Year 4 Challenge Textbook page 46

Small sticky notes; 1–1000 number line (optional)

Abacus Evolve objectives

- **Y5** Use known number facts and place value for mental addition and subtraction
- **Y5** Develop further the relationship between addition and subtraction
- **Y5** Use known number facts and place value for mental addition and subtraction of decimals
- **Y5** Mentally add or subtract a pair of decimal numbers, crossing units or tenths
- **Y5** Subtract one integer from another, each less than 10 000, using informal written methods

Framework objectives

- **Y5** *Use efficient written methods to add and subtract whole numbers and decimals with up to two places*
- **Y5** *Present a spoken argument, sequencing points logically, defending views with evidence and making use of persuasive language*

Teacher notes

Activity
- Write a simple subtraction sentence, e.g. $24 - 8 = 16$. Cover each of the numbers in turn and point out that when a number is hidden, a problem is created. *How can we work out the missing number?* Encourage answers involving the inverse operation.
- Each child writes a subtraction number sentence. They check it is correct, then cover one number with a sticky note. They take turns to show their problem to the group, who solve it.
- Children work from Textbook page 46. They solve missing-number subtraction problems.
- They then follow these steps: generate pairs of 3-digit numbers; find the difference; subtract each of the 3-digit numbers from 1000; find the difference between these two numbers. Children do this for different pairs of 3-digit numbers, and describe what they notice.

Further extension
Children can use a 1–1000 number line to explain why the difference between two 3-digit numbers and their complements to 1000 are the same.

If you have time
Children can make up their own number sentences with two missing numbers, such as ☐ − 47 = ☐. They try them out on a partner. They will find that there are many possible solutions. Ask children to look for a connection between the first missing number and the second missing number in each solution. (In this case the numbers always have a difference of 47.)

Be aware

- Children who reach the Extra activity may not initially realise the added challenge of balancing the needs of two different conditions. Encourage them to use known number facts to reach an answer.

Outcomes

- I can add and subtract to solve missing-number problems.

D2: adding by partitioning; subtracting 2- and 3-digit numbers; adding and subtracting near multiples of 10; adding HTU

Summary

Y4 ⭐ D2.5

The bill

Individuals, pairs or groups working independently

Year 4 Challenge Textbook page 47

Year 4 Challenge PCM 31

Abacus Evolve objectives

- Add HTU + TU, HTU + HTU using informal written methods
- Add more than two numbers using standard written methods
- Add amounts of money, e.g. £3·26 + £5·85, using standard written methods
- Compare and order amounts of money
- Recognise decimal notation in the context of money

Framework objectives

- Refine and use efficient written methods to add and subtract 2-digit and 3-digit whole numbers and £·p
- Use decimal notation for tenths and hundredths and partition decimals; relate the notation to money and measurement; position 1-place and 2-place decimals on a number line
- Solve one-step and two-step problems involving numbers, money or measures, including time; choose and carry out appropriate calculations, using calculator methods where appropriate
- Represent a puzzle or problem using number sentences, statements or diagrams; use these to solve the problem; present and interpret the solution in the context of the problem

Teacher notes

Preparation
Photocopy PCM 31, one copy per child, pair or group.

Getting started
Together read through the introduction on the Textbook page. Check that children understand how the friends' preferences indicate what they order from the menu.

Activity
Children work from Textbook page 47. They use the information from the Textbook page to work out what food Amie, Bart and Chan ordered from the menu on PCM 31. Children are then shown an accounting grid to represent and organise this information. They copy and complete the grid to check their answers.

Extra help
Before the main activity children can practise choosing meals from the menu and calculating their own bill.

If you have time
Children can use the menu to devise other combinations of food and drinks to fit within certain budgets, or to be as near as possible to selected amounts.

Be aware

- Though the calculations are relatively straightforward, children may initially have trouble interpreting the story context and identifying the necessary calculations.

Outcomes

- I can add and subtract amounts of money.
- I can solve a set of problems, record my solutions and use a checking grid.

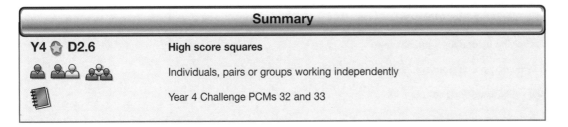

D2: adding by partitioning; subtracting 2- and 3-digit numbers; adding and subtracting near multiples of 10; adding HTU

Summary

Y4 ⬠ D2.6

High score squares

Individuals, pairs or groups working independently

Year 4 Challenge PCMs 32 and 33

Abacus Evolve objectives

- Add HTU + TU, HTU + HTU using informal written methods
- Subtract HTU − TU, HTU − HTU using informal written method of complementary addition

Framework objectives

- Refine and use efficient written methods to add and subtract 2-digit and 3-digit whole numbers and £·p
- Suggest a line of enquiry and the strategy needed to follow it; collect, organise and interpret selected information to find answers
- Report solutions to puzzles and problems, giving explanations and reasoning orally and in writing, using diagrams and symbols
- Respond appropriately to others in the light of alternative viewpoints

Teacher notes

Preparation
Photocopy PCMs 32 and 33, one copy of PCM 32 and several copies of PCM 33 per child, pair or group.

Activity
Children read the instructions on PCM 32. They learn how to make a 'high score square'. They are shown a high score square with a score of 270. Children follow the steps and fill in one of the blank high score squares on PCM 33. They aim to find a square with a score higher than 270. They then investigate how to find the square with the highest possible score.

Further extension
Try to find the score nearest to 0. Is it possible to have a score of exactly 0? Can you make a score of exactly 1000? Any other given 3-digit number?

Information
It is possible to reach negative scores on the high score squares.

Be aware

- Children will need to consider the implications of 'trade-offs' when placing digits in their square. For example, when increasing a row number, the column number will also increase and the impact on the difference may be far less than expected.

Outcomes

- I can investigate and improve my score in a number problem.
- I can keep track of solutions and change them to find better ones.

E2: ×6 multiplication/division facts; ×8 multiplication/division facts; compare and order fractions; decimal and fraction forms of $\frac{1}{2}$s and $\frac{1}{10}$s

Summary

Y4 ✦ E2.1

Multiplying by doubling and halving

Individuals, pairs or groups working independently

Year 4 Challenge Textbook page 48

Year 4 Challenge PCM 34

Calculators

Abacus Evolve objectives

- Double or halve 2-digit numbers by doubling or halving the tens first
- Derive doubles of integers up to 50 and the corresponding halves
- Use doubling or halving to find new facts from known facts

Framework objectives

- Identify the doubles of 2-digit numbers; use to calculate doubles of multiples of 10 and 100 and derive the corresponding halves

Teacher notes

Getting started

Introduce children to the 'peasant' method of multiplication by doubling and halving. Ask children to discuss how this method might work. (When you double one side of a multiplication and halve the other side, the product remains the same. As numbers in the halving column with remainders are rounded down, other numbers in the doubling column must be added on to make sure the final product is the same and gives the right answer.)

Activity

Children work from Textbook page 48. They read about peasant multiplication and learn the method. They then use PCM 34 to complete three multiplications using this method.
Children then check three multiplications to see if they are correct. They rewrite the multiplications correctly using the peasant method.

Extra help

When checking the incorrect tables, encourage children to look at the halving column to see if the numbers are odd or even.

Further extension

Children can create multiplications on a calculator then give a partner some divisions to check, giving alternative answers. For example, $23 \times 17 = 391$. The partner checks if 391 divided by 23 equals 15, 17 or 19.

Information

This method of multiplication has been the most widely used for several millennia. It is still the most commonly used method as it can be used by people who have not learnt to multiply or divide beyond doubling and halving. It has several names including peasant multiplication, Egyptian multiplication and Russian multiplication.

Be aware

- Children who can double and halve may find adding several numbers accurately to be the difficulty. Allow calculator checks of this if necessary.

Outcomes

- I can double and halve numbers.
- I can multiply using a different method.

Supporting resources

Children can read more about the peasant method and how it works, here:
- http://mathforum.org/dr.math/faq/faq.peasant.html

Challenge Plan: Year 4

E2: ×6 multiplication/division facts; ×8 multiplication/division facts; compare and order fractions; decimal and fraction forms of $\frac{1}{2}$s and $\frac{1}{10}$s

Summary

Y4 ⬡ E2.2 | **Maximising products**

Pairs or groups working independently

Year 4 Challenge Textbook page 49

Digit cards 0–9; × and = cards; calculators

Abacus Evolve objectives

- Know by heart the multiplication facts for the 2, 3, 4, 5 and 10 times tables
- Know the multiplication facts for the 6 times table, and the corresponding division facts
- Begin to know the multiplication facts for the 7 times table, and the corresponding division facts
- Begin to know the multiplication facts for the 8 times table, and the corresponding division facts
- Begin to know the multiplication facts for the 9 times table, and the corresponding division facts
- Understand and use the commutativity of multiplication
- Multiply TU × U by partitioning into T and U
- Multiply TU × U using informal written methods: grid method

Framework objectives

- *Derive and recall multiplication facts up to 10 × 10, the corresponding division facts and multiples of numbers to 10 up to the tenth multiple*
- *Develop and use written methods to record, support and explain multiplication and division of two-digit numbers by a 1-digit number, including division with remainders (e.g. 15 × 9, 98 ÷ 6)*
- Identify and use patterns, relationships and properties of numbers or shapes; investigate a statement involving numbers and test it with examples

Teacher notes

Preparation
Make one × card and one = card for each pair or group.

Getting started
Run through the concept of maximising the product of multiplications, made from digit cards, using the example on the Textbook page. Give each pair or group a set of digit cards 0–9, a × card and an = card.

Activity
Children work from Textbook page 49. They are shown six different ways of placing three digit cards, a × sign and an = sign. They find the six products and identify the largest.
Children then use sets of three digit cards and try to find the maximum product in each case. They compare their results and check them using a calculator. They discuss any patterns they can see in the placement of the digits for the maximum products.
Children then use four digit cards and make a TU × TU multiplication. They try to find the maximum product. They compare their results with a partner and discuss any patterns they notice.

Extra help
Children can use the grid method to help with multiplying by partitioning. For example 42 × 3 = 126.

×	40	2
3	120	6

If you have time
Children can investigate the maximum products when five digit cards are arranged to make an HTU × TU multiplication.

Be aware

- If children are looking for patterns in the placing of the digit cards they may find it useful to pursue the grid method of multiplication. This can reveal patterns more readily than standard written methods of multiplication.

Outcomes

- I can find the maximum product in a set of multiplications.
- I can find patterns in multiplications.

Challenge Plan: Year 4

E2: ×6 multiplication/division facts; ×8 multiplication/division facts; compare and order fractions; decimal and fraction forms of $\frac{1}{2}$s and $\frac{1}{10}$s

Summary

Y4 ☆ E2.3

Into the unknown

A small group working with an adult

Year 4 Challenge Textbook page 50

Year 4 Challenge PCM 35

Abacus Evolve objectives

- **Y5** Know by heart all multiplication facts up to 10 × 10
- **Y5** Derive quickly division facts corresponding to multiplication facts up to 10 × 10
- **Y5** Recognise that from one multiplication or division fact, others can be found
- **Y5** Multiply or divide any integer up to 10 000 by 10 or 100 and understand the effect
- **Y5** Recognise and explain patterns and relationships, generalise and predict

Framework objectives

- **Y5** Recall quickly multiplication facts up to 10 × 10, use to multiply pairs of multiples of 10 and 100 and derive quickly corresponding division facts
- **Y5** Use understanding of place value to multiply and divide whole numbers and decimals by 10, 100 or 1000
- **Y5** Explore patterns, properties and relationships and propose a general statement involving numbers or shapes; identify examples for which the statement is true or false

Teacher notes

Preparation
Photocopy PCM 35, one copy per child.

Activity
- Use the example on the Textbook page to introduce the idea of moving from known facts to unknown facts. *If 4 × 8 = 32, what is 40 × 8?* Encourage children to recognise that one multiplier has been multiplied by 10 so the product will be multiplied by 10 too. Together find the answers to all of the unknown facts in the example.
- Write *3 × 7 = 21. Tell me some new facts using this fact.* Ask each child in the group to contribute at least one fact.
- Children work from Textbook page 50. They complete the number facts related to 5 × 9 = 45 and 7 × 8 = 56 on PCM 35 and add any of their own.
- Look at the second half of the Textbook page. *40 × 32 looks like a difficult sum. How can we make it easier?* Encourage answers that relate to multiplying 32 by 4 (e.g. by doubling it, then doubling it again), then multiplying by 10. Check that children understand how this calculation has been broken down into simpler calculations.
- Children complete the Textbook page, breaking the multiplications down into simpler steps to solve them.

Further extension
Each child chooses a 2-digit number. Write the numbers where children can see them. Each child chooses two numbers and makes a multiplication calculation, then finds the answer using a calculator. For example 23 × 51 = 1173. Ask children to add 1 to the multiplier and subtract 1 from the multiplicard, or vice-versa. Then find the answer. For example 24 × 50 = 1200 or 22 × 52 = 1144. Children explore how this has changed the answers and why that might be.

Be aware
- Children may believe that to multiply by 10, you can simply add a zero. However this can lead to errors such as 8 × 70p = £560. Encourage children to always use the full expression of numbers and processes to avoid such errors.

Outcomes
- I can make new multiplication and division facts from a multiplication fact that I know.
- I can see how a set of multiplications and divisions are related.

Supporting resources
You can find an A3 poster showing clouds of connections, here:
- http://www.atm.org.uk/buyonline/products/vis006.html

Challenge Plan: Year 4

E2: ×6 multiplication/division facts; ×8 multiplication/division facts; compare and order fractions; decimal and fraction forms of $\frac{1}{2}$s and $\frac{1}{10}$s

Summary

Y4 ⬡ E2.4

Sharing camels

Pairs or groups working independently

Year 4 Challenge Textbook page 51

Linking cubes

Abacus Evolve objectives

- **Y5** Relate fractions to division
- **Y5** Use division to find fractions, including tenths and hundredths of numbers and quantities
- **Y5** Use fraction notation, including mixed numbers, and the vocabulary 'numerator' and 'denominator'
- **Y5** Recognise and explain patterns and relationships, generalise and predict

Framework objectives

- **Y5** Find fractions using division (e.g. $\frac{1}{100}$ of 5 kg), and percentages of numbers and quantities (e.g. 10%, 5% and 15% of £80)
- **Y5** Express a smaller whole number as a fraction of a larger one (e.g. recognise that 5 out of 8 is $\frac{5}{8}$); find equivalent fractions (e.g. $\frac{7}{10} = \frac{14}{20}$, or $\frac{19}{10} = 1\frac{9}{10}$); relate fractions to their decimal representations
- **Y5** Plan and pursue an enquiry; present evidence by collecting, organising and interpreting information; suggest extensions to the enquiry

Teacher notes

Getting started

Read through the problem on the Textbook page together. Ask children to lay out linking cubes to represent the camels. Children solve the problem. They should recognise that with the given fractions of 17 camels they do not have whole numbers. However the fractions of 18 camels are whole numbers and the remainder is also a whole number. Explain to children that they will only be working with unit fractions, $\frac{1}{2}$, $\frac{1}{3}$, $\frac{1}{4}$ and so on.

Activity

Children work from Textbook page 51. They investigate solving the problem with some different numbers of camels, of their choosing. Children then investigate how to solve the problem if there are 17 camels but a different number of children. They then make up their own story like this and solve it.

If you have time

What if the man has two children and they are twins? They each want the same share of the camels. Children explore the possibilities in this situation.

Extra help

Children should work backwards from the unit fraction share, to find the total number. When looking for patterns children should find that the denominators of the unit fractions must be factors of the total number of camels.

Be aware

- Children may not initially see why these fractions cannot be made. The use of practical, indivisible objects like linking cubes will help them to see this.

Outcomes

- I can find unit fractions of some whole numbers.
- I can recognise which unit fractions of whole numbers give a whole number.
- I can make up a story about unit fractions.

Challenge Plan: Year 4

Summary

Y4 ⬟ E2.5

Fractions in order

Pairs or groups working independently

Year 4 Challenge Textbook page 52

Year 4 Challenge PCMs 36 and 37

Abacus Evolve objectives

- Compare and order fractions
- Locate fractions on a number line
- Recognise mixed numbers
- Use decimal notation for tenths
- Recognise the equivalence between the decimal and fraction forms of halves and tenths

Framework objectives

- Use diagrams to identify equivalent fractions (e.g. $\frac{6}{8}$ and $\frac{3}{4}$, or $\frac{70}{100}$ and $\frac{7}{10}$); interpret mixed numbers and position them on a number line (e.g. $3\frac{1}{2}$)
- Recognise the equivalence between decimal and fraction forms of one half, quarters, tenths and hundredths

Teacher notes

Preparation
Photocopy PCMs 36 and 37, one copy of each per pair. Cut out the cards on PCM 36.

Getting started
Look at the kites and number line on PCM 36. Children discuss how we know where each number is on the number line.

Activity
Children work from Textbook page 52. They work together to locate the kite numbers on the number line on PCM 37. They then play the two fraction games in pairs.

Further extension
Children can make their own sets of cards for these games.

Be aware

- Children may find it difficult to see the relationship between fraction families, such as halves, fifths and tenths, and compare them.

Outcomes

- I can compare fractions, including halves, quarters, fifths and tenths.
- I can come up with a strategy for playing a fraction-ordering game.

Supporting resources

Some other fraction ordering games can be found here:
- http://themathgames.com/

E2: ×6 multiplication/division facts; ×8 multiplication/division facts; compare and order fractions; decimal and fraction forms of $\frac{1}{2}$s and $\frac{1}{10}$s

Summary

Y4 ✦ E2.6

Tenths link cards

A small group working with an adult

Year 4 Challenge PCM 38

Thin card

Abacus Evolve objectives

- Use decimal notation for tenths
- Recognise the equivalence between the decimal and fraction forms of halves and tenths
- Say one or more numbers lying between two given numbers
- Recognise decimal notation in the context of money

Framework objectives

- Recognise the equivalence between decimal and fraction forms of one half, quarters, tenths and hundredths
- Use decimal notation for tenths and hundredths and partition decimals; relate the notation to money and measurement; position 1-place and 2-place decimals on a number line

Teacher notes

Preparation
Photocopy PCM 38 onto thin A4 card, one copy per pair or group. Cut out the cards.

Activity
- Practise moving from halves, fifths and tenths to decimals.
  What are 25 halves? (12·5) What are 21 fifths? (4·2) What are 33 tenths? (3·3)
- Practise saying how many tenths there are in decimal numbers.
  How many tenths in 1·2? (12) How many tenths in 2·8? (28)
- Practise finding the number half-way between two decimals with tenths.
  What is half-way between 2·2 and 2·8? (2·5) What is half-way between 1·3 and 2·1? (1·7)
- Give each pair or group a set of six linking cards from PCM 38. (The sets are labelled A, B, C and D.) The solution to each question is on another card. Children solve each question to link the cards into a chain.
- When children complete one chain, give them another set of cards, until they have completed all four chains.
- Bring the group together. Shuffle all 24 cards together and deal them out. Ask a child whose card has the answer 2·4 written on it to start. They read out the question on their card. Players take turns to play the next card or 'pass', until one player has no cards left and is the winner.

If you have time
Play the game again, but faster. Allow a 'play when you can go' rule rather than asking children to take turns.

Information
In a set of six cards any card may be placed first in the chain, as they form a loop of six cards.

Be aware

- As children are dealing with several ideas together they may need considerable time to think about answers. Reassure them that understanding and making connections is more important than speed.

Outcomes

- I can find how many halves, fifths and tenths in a decimal number.
- I can find a decimal with tenths that is half-way between two other decimals.

Summary

Y4 ⭐ A3.1

Rounding link cards

A small group working with an adult

Year 4 Challenge PCMs 39 and 40

Abacus Evolve objectives

- Round a 3-digit number to the nearest 10 or 100
- Round a sum of money to the nearest pound
- Make and justify estimates up to about 250
- Use known number facts and place value to multiply or divide mentally
- Know by heart the multiplication facts for the 2, 3, 4, 5 and 10 times tables
- Know the multiplication facts for the 6 times table, and the corresponding division facts

Framework objectives

- Partition, round and order 4-digit whole numbers; use positive and negative numbers in context and position them on a number line; state inequalities using the symbols $<$ and $>$, e.g. $^-3 > ^-5$, $^-1 < ^+1$
- Use knowledge of rounding, number operations and inverses to estimate and check calculations
- Derive and recall multiplication facts up to 10×10, the corresponding division facts and multiples of numbers to 10 up to the tenth multiple
- Solve one-step and two-step problems involving numbers, money or measures, including time; choose and carry out appropriate calculations, using calculator methods where appropriate
- Respond appropriately to others in the light of alternative viewpoints

Teacher notes

Preparation
Photocopy PCMs 39 and 40, one copy of each per pair or group. Cut out the cards.

Activity
- Discuss rounding amounts of money to the nearest 10p, 50p, £1, £2, £5 and £10.
- Give each pair or group a set of six cards from PCM 39. (The sets are labelled A, B, C and D.) Children estimate the multiplication, rounding to the nearest £10. The solution to each question is on another card. Children solve each question to link the cards into a chain. The multipliers used are ×3, ×4, ×5 and ×6.
- As they complete one chain, give them another set of cards, until they have completed all four chains.
- Bring the group together. Shuffle all 24 cards together and deal them out. Children take turns to read out the question on their card. Players take turns to play the next card or 'pass', until one player has no cards left and is the winner.
- Give each pair or group a set of six cards from PCM 40. Children play this game as a group, estimating the multiplications, and rounding to the nearest £5.

Further extension
Children can work in pairs to devise their own chains of six linking cards, rounding to the nearest £10, then the nearest £5. They follow the structure of the cards on the PCMs but work with higher values (up to £500 or £1000 as appropriate). Children should give answers in a combination of pounds and multiples of 10p.

If you have time
Play the games again, but faster. Allow a 'play when you can go' rule rather than asking children to take turns.

Be aware

- Children may incorrectly partition when multiplying, for example they may partition 14×3 as $(10 \times 3) + 4 = 34$. You could ask one of the other children in the group to explain the partitioning process clearly to the others.

Outcomes

- I can round money to the nearest £1, £5 and £10.
- I can use rounding to make estimates in my head.
- I can multiply numbers by 2, 3, 4, 5 and 6.
- I can use partitioning to multiply larger numbers.

Supporting resources

Play the 'Rounding game' at:
- www.primaryresources.co.uk/maths/mathsB8.htm

or practise the times-tables using this interactive game:
- www.bbc.co.uk/schools/ks2bitesize/maths/activities/multiplication.shtml

Summary

Y4 ⭐ A3.2

Estimating perimeters and areas

Individuals, pairs or groups working independently

Year 4 Challenge Textbook page 53

Calculators

Abacus Evolve objectives

- **Y5** Round a number with one decimal place to the nearest whole number
- **Y5** Know by heart all multiplication facts up to 10 × 10
- **Y5** Continue to multiply TU × U by partitioning into T and U
- **Y5** Understand area measured in square centimetres
- **Y5** Understand, measure and calculate perimeters of rectangles

Framework objectives

- **Y5** Explain what each digit represents in whole numbers and decimals with up to two places, and partition, round and order these numbers
- **Y5** Extend mental methods for whole-number calculations, for example to multiply a 2-digit by 1-digit number (e.g. 12 × 9), to multiply by 25 (e.g. 16 × 25), to subtract one near-multiple of 1000 from another (e.g. 6070 − 4097)
- **Y5** Draw and measure lines to the nearest millimetre; measure and calculate the perimeter of regular and irregular polygons; use the formula for the area of a rectangle to calculate its area
- **Y5** Represent a problem by identifying and recording the calculations needed to solve it; find possible solutions and confirm them in the context of the problem

Teacher notes

Getting started

Check that children understand perimeter and area of a rectangle and know how they are calculated.

Read through the introduction to the Textbook page together and make sure children see why the area and perimeter are rounded up and down.

Activity

Children work from Textbook page 53. They learn that the perimeter and area of measured rectangles are approximate and have been rounded up or down. Children think about the minimum and maximum lengths, perimeters and areas. Without calculators, they find the upper and lower limits for the perimeter and area of some rectangles that have been measured to the nearest cm.

Further extension

Write $\frac{1}{2} \times \frac{1}{2} = \frac{1}{4}$. Then write $2 \times 2 = 4$. *What do you notice?* (The same multiplication fact is used in both calculations.) Remind children that $\times\frac{1}{2}$ is the same as 'find half of' or $\div 2$. Children find more unit fraction calculations that use multiplication facts and use arrays to demonstrate why this is. For example $2 \times 3 = 6$ and $\frac{1}{2} \times \frac{1}{3} = \frac{1}{6}$.

If you have time

Groups can check their work with calculators, then use calculators to find patterns in the perimeters and areas of squares measured to the nearest cm.

Be aware

- The multiplication $\frac{1}{2} \times \frac{1}{2}$ may confuse children. They do not need to know how to multiply fractions, but should understand that half of a half is a quarter.
- Children may be familiar with rounding, but may not be used to considering totals after they have already been rounded.

Outcomes

- I can work out the maximum and minimum lengths of a line if I know what the measurement has been rounded to.
- I can calculate the perimeter of a rectangle.
- I can use a grid to calculate the area of a rectangle.

Supporting resources

This 'Shape builder' tool, allows pupils to build their own shape then calculate the perimeter and area:
- www.shodor.org/interactivate/textbooks/chapter/7/209/

Summary

Y4 ⭐ A3.3

The Gattegno chart

Individuals, pairs or groups working independently

Year 4 Challenge Textbook page 54

Year 4 Challenge PCM 41

Abacus Evolve objectives

- Begin to multiply integers by 100
- Multiply or divide any integer up to 1000 by 10 and understand the effect
- Use known number facts and place value to multiply or divide mentally
- Use doubling or halving to find new facts from known facts
- Read and write numbers up to 100 000 in figures and words
- Know what each digit in a 5-digit number represents
- Recognise the relationship between Th, H, T and U

Framework objectives

- Multiply and divide numbers to 1000 by 10 and then 100 (whole number answers), understanding the effect; relate to scaling up or down
- Identify the doubles of 2-digit numbers; use these to calculate doubles of multiples of 10 and 100 and derive the corresponding halves
- Partition, round and order 4-digit whole numbers; use positive and negative numbers in context and position them on a number line; state inequalities using the symbols $<$ and $>$ (e.g. $^-3 > ^-5$, $^-1 < ^+1$)
- Identify and use patterns, relationships and properties of numbers or shapes; investigate a statement involving numbers and test it with examples

Teacher notes

Preparation
Photocopy PCM 41, one copy per child.

Activity
Children work from Textbook page 54. They read about Caleb Gattegno's chart and how to use it. Children are shown how to multiply by 10 using the Gattegno chart on PCM 41. They then explore multiplying by 100 and dividing by 10 and 100 using the chart. Children work out how to multiply and divide by the other powers of 10 on the chart.
Children then try using the Gattegno chart to multiply and divide by more complicated numbers, using doubling and halving (for example to multiply by 2000).

Further extension
Use the Gattegno chart to introduce index notation (powers) for very large numbers.
Look at 7000 on the table. We can think of it as 7 × 1000. It takes three ×10 steps to get from 7 to 7000. To show this, we can write 7×10^3. Children explore index notation for other 4-digit numbers.

Be aware

- Children may think of multiplying by powers of 10 in terms of adding zeros to a number. This should be discouraged as it is unreliable when moving to decimals (e.g. $2 \cdot 3 \times 10$ is not $2 \cdot 30$). It is sounder for children to think of ×10 as each digit moving up a place value, becoming 10 times as big.
- Children are unlikely to be familiar with index notation at this stage. However Gattegno's chart is a useful tool for introducing it at a basic level if you feel children are ready.

Outcomes

- I can multiply and divide numbers by 10, 100 and 1000.
- I can explain what happens to the hundred, tens and units of a number when it is multiplied by 10, 100 and 1000.
- I can use what I know to multiply and divide by numbers such as 2000.
- I know what each digit in a 5-digit number represents.
- I can read and write numbers up to 100 000.

Supporting resources

Children identify the value of each digit in a 7-digit number in this bingo game:
- nrich.maths.org/public/viewer.php?obj_id=1288

Summary

Y4 ⭐ A3.4	**Subtraction walls**
👥	Groups working independently
📖	Year 4 Challenge Textbook page 55
📓	Year 4 Challenge PCM 42

Abacus Evolve objectives

- Subtract HTU − TU, HTU − HTU using informal written method of complementary addition
- Understand the principles (not the names) of the commutative and associative laws as they apply or not to addition and subtraction
- Use known number facts and place value to subtract one 2-digit number from another, by counting on and back
- Consolidate understanding of the relationship between addition and subtraction
- Find a small difference by counting on, e.g. 5003 − 4996

Framework objectives

- Refine and use efficient written methods to add and subtract 2-digit and 3-digit whole numbers and £·p
- *Add or subtract mentally pairs of two-digit whole numbers (e.g. 47 + 58, 91 − 35)*
- Use knowledge of addition and subtraction facts and place value to derive sums and differences of pairs of multiples of 10, 100 or 1000
- Suggest a line of enquiry and the strategy needed to follow it; collect, organise and interpret selected information to find answers
- Use time, resources and group members efficiently by distributing tasks, checking progress, making back-up plans

Teacher notes

Preparation
Photocopy PCM 42, one copy per child.

Activity
Children work from Textbook page 55. They explore number walls where adjacent numbers are added or subtracted to form the next row of numbers. Children use the blank number walls on PCM 42 to solve problems investigating subtraction walls.
They then make their own subtraction wall problems that fulfil certain criteria.

Extra help
Provide children with blank number walls for them to practise addition and subtraction with smaller numbers first. This will ensure that they understand how to complete the walls before moving on to the main activity.

If you have time
Children can remove some of the numbers from their number walls, then swap and try to solve each other's.

Be aware

- Children may not see how to begin working with the limited starting information on a number wall. Encourage them to ask questions such as *What do I add to this number to make the next one? How many more is this number than the last one? How do I find the difference between these numbers?*

Outcomes

- I can think of subtraction as counting on from one number to another.
- I can work out additions and subtractions by writing calculations.
- I can add and subtract numbers in my head.
- I can investigate patterns using my own examples.

Supporting resources

Number walls can be found in many resources, including 'Add and subtract pyramids' at:
- www.eriding.net/maths/pyramids.shtml

Summary

Y4 ✦ A3.5	**Matching subtractions**
	A small group working with an adult
	Year 4 Challenge Textbook page 56
	Year 4 Challenge PCM 43

Abacus Evolve objectives

- Subtract HTU − TU, HTU − HTU using standard written method of decomposition
- Understand the principles (not the names) of the commutative and associative laws as they apply or not to addition and subtraction
- Find what to add to a 2- or 3-digit number to make 100 or the next multiple of 100
- Find what to add to a 4-digit multiple of 100 to make the next multiple of 1000
- Consolidate understanding of the relationship between addition and subtraction
- Add and subtract 2- and 3-digit multiples of 10

Framework objectives

- Refine and use efficient written methods to add and subtract 2-digit and 3-digit whole numbers and £·p
- *Add or subtract mentally pairs of two-digit whole numbers (e.g. 47 + 58, 91 − 35)*
- Use knowledge of addition and subtraction facts and place value to derive sums and differences of pairs of multiples of 10, 100 or 1000
- Use and reflect on some ground rules for dialogue (e.g. making structured, extended contributions, speaking audibly, making meaning explicit and listening actively)

Teacher notes

Preparation
Photocopy PCM 43, one copy per group. Cut out the cards.

Activity
Introduce the idea of finding subtractions with the same answer. Start with 216 − 148. Look at the number line on the Textbook page. Stress that the subtraction is the distance from 148 to 216. *Can you change the subtraction but keep the answer the same? Moving both numbers 'up 2' gives 218 − 150.* Write *216 − 148* then draw a line from this to *218 − 150*. Ask for new suggestions, write them up and join them to the original subtraction with a line. Children check each other's suggestions. Children should recognise that if the distance between the numbers is the same then the answer to the subtraction will be the same.

Children work from Textbook page 56. They use the number facts discussed above to simplify subtractions in order to calculate them mentally.

Children then use cards from PCM 43 to find matching subtractions. Children work out the answers to all the subtractions (they could write the answers on the backs of the cards), then sort the cards according to their answers, looking for a pattern. They try to find the missing subtractions in the sequence and, if possible, extend the sequence in both directions.

Extra help
Ask children to explore finding as many subtractions as they can with the answer 20 (for example, 90 − 70 = 20, 80 − 60 = 20, 70 − 50 = 20). Children look for patterns in their subtraction calculations. This will introduce the idea of many calculations having the same answer.

Be aware

- Children may need practical experience of adding/subtracting the same amount to small numbers, and finding that it does not change the difference, before building up to larger numbers.

Outcomes

- I can use a number line to subtract large numbers.
- I can work out subtractions by counting on.
- I can find new subtractions with the same answer.
- I can spot patterns and fill in missing subtractions.

Supporting resources

Children can try the 'Subtraction connect four' game at:
- www.teachingideas.co.uk/maths/contents06additionsubtraction.htm

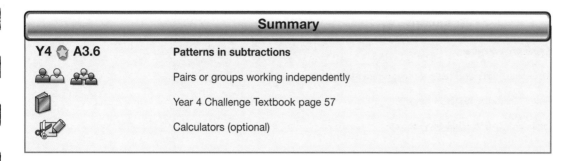

Challenge Plan: Year 4

A3: rounding numbers and estimating; multiplying/dividing by 10/100/5/20; subtracting HTU − TU, HTU − HTU

Summary

Y4 ⭐ A3.6

Patterns in subtractions

Pairs or groups working independently

Year 4 Challenge Textbook page 57

Calculators (optional)

Abacus Evolve objectives

- **Y5** Subtract one integer from another, each less than 10 000, using informal written methods
- **Y5** Subtract one integer from another, each less than 10 000, using standard written methods
- **Y5** Make general statements about odd or even numbers, including their sums and differences
- **Y5** Recognise and explain patterns and relationships, generalise and predict

Framework objectives

- **Y5** *Use efficient written methods to add and subtract whole numbers and decimals with up to two places*
- **Y5** Plan and pursue an enquiry; present evidence by collecting, organising and interpreting information; suggest extensions to the enquiry
- **Y5** Explore patterns, properties and relationships and propose a general statement involving numbers or shapes
- **Y5** Plan and manage a group task over time by using different levels of planning

Teacher notes

Getting started
Run through the example on the Textbook page and check that children understand how to generate their own subtraction patterns.

Activity
Children work from Textbook page 57. They make their own subtraction patterns using numbers with consecutive digits, e.g. 432 − 234.
They then look for patterns in subtractions involving consecutive even-digit numbers (e.g. 642 − 246) and consecutive odd-digit numbers (753 − 357).
Children then explore a range of more advanced patterns, including 4-digit and 5-digit variations and money amounts in decimal format. You can either allow children to use calculators, or ask them to use their favourite written method for solving the subtractions.

Extra help
Children can practise finding subtraction patterns by reversing 2-digit numbers, for example 75 − 57 = 18, 41 − 14 = 27. They should notice that all the answers are multiples of 9.

Information
This is one of the patterns children will investigate. Each of the digits increases by 1 each time.
630 − 036 = 594
741 − 147 = 594
852 − 258 = 594
As children are working with consecutive numbers, they will find that the answer always stays the same for each pattern. This is because the difference between each digit is always the same.

Be aware

- Children who are able to carry out the subtractions may still need support in investigating the patterns systematically, if they are still acquiring this skill.

Outcomes

- I can investigate patterns in number subtractions and explain them.

Supporting resources

There are a selection of activities using different patterns of numbers for children to investigate here:
- www.teachingideas.co.uk/maths/contents05nopatterns.htm

Challenge Plan: Year 4

B3: finding differences and relating addition and subtraction; ×9 facts; 8-point compass and turns; angles in degrees

Summary

Y4 ⬡ B3.1

Kaprekar's numbers

Individuals, pairs or groups working independently

Year 4 Challenge Textbook page 58

Digit cards 0–9; calculators (optional)

Abacus Evolve objectives

- Find a small difference by counting on, e.g. 5003 − 4996
- Subtract HTU − TU, HTU − HTU using standard written method of decomposition
- Add HTU + TU, HTU + HTU using standard written methods
- Begin to know the multiplication facts for the 9 times table, and the corresponding division facts
- Make and investigate a general statement about familiar numbers or shapes by finding examples that satisfy it (number)
- Recognise and explain patterns and relationships, generalise and predict

Framework objectives

- Use knowledge of addition and subtraction facts and place value to derive sums and differences of pairs of multiples of 10, 100 or 1000
- Refine and use efficient written methods to add and subtract two-digit and three-digit whole numbers and £·p
- *Derive and recall multiplication facts up to 10 × 10, the corresponding division facts and multiples of numbers to 10 up to the tenth multiple*
- Identify and use patterns, relationships and properties of numbers or shapes; investigate a statement involving numbers and test it with examples
- Solve one-step and two-step problems involving numbers, money or measures, including time; choose and carry out appropriate calculations, using calculator methods where appropriate

Teacher notes

Getting started
Read together about Kaprekar and the process leading to Kaprekar's constant, 1089. Run through the process for 3-digit numbers, and explain what to do if there is a zero in the units place, as in 320 − 023.

Activity
Children work from Textbook page 58. They learn how to find Kaprekar's constant and Kaprekar's number, then use digit cards to explore them further.

Further extension
Children could try the '1089' method using starting numbers with five or more digits. Using calculators or tests of divisibility they could check whether all the end numbers are multiples of 9.

If you have time
Children can generate 'hiccup' numbers by repeating a 3-digit number to make a 6-digit number, for example 267267. They use calculators to divide their 'hiccup' numbers by 5, 6, 7… up to 15. *Which numbers can you divide by exactly?* (7, 11 and 13.)

Be aware

- Children may already know that a number is a multiple of 9 if the sum of the digits is divisible by 9. The second web link below provides support with this concept. Encourage children to multiply by 9 using multiplying by 10 and then subtracting the number.

Outcomes

- I can check to see if a number is a multiple of 9 by dividing by 9 on my calculator.
- I can investigate number patterns and find other examples that work.
- I can add and subtract 2- and 3-digit numbers on paper.
- I can add and subtract 4- and 5-digit numbers using a calculator.

Supporting resources

Kaprekar's work is well illustrated at:
- http://www.math.hmc.edu/funfacts/ffiles/10002.5-8.shtml

A good method for working out the 9 times table using your fingers:
- http://www.multiplication.com/lesson10_nines_fingers.htm

Divisibility tests for various numbers:
- http://nrich.maths.org/public/viewer.php?obj_id=1308

Challenge Plan: Year 4

B3: finding differences and relating addition and subtraction; ×9 facts; 8-point compass and turns; angles in degrees

Summary

Y4 ☆ B3.2 — **Multiplying and dividing by 9**

A small group working with an adult

Year 4 Challenge Textbook page 59

Year 4 Challenge PCM 44

A3 card (optional)

Abacus Evolve objectives

- Begin to know the multiplication facts for the 9 times table, and the corresponding division facts
- Consolidate division as the inverse of multiplication
- Recognise and explain patterns and relationships, generalise and predict

Framework objectives

- *Derive and recall multiplication facts up to 10 × 10, the corresponding division facts and multiples of numbers to 10 up to the tenth multiple*
- *Develop and use written methods to record, support and explain multiplication and division of two-digit numbers by a one-digit number, including division with remainders (e.g. 15 × 9, 98 ÷ 6)*
- Solve one-step and two-step problems involving numbers, money or measures, including time; choose and carry out appropriate calculations, using calculator methods where appropriate
- Respond appropriately to others in the light of alternative viewpoints

Teacher notes

Preparation
Photocopy PCM 44 (onto A3 card if possible). Cut out card sets A and B and keep them separate.

Activity
- Ask children to give the answers to some simple ×9 facts, e.g. 4×9, 8×9, $81 \div 9$.
- *What is 47×9?* Explain that there is a simple way to work this out, using the grid method shown on Textbook page 59. Use the grids to introduce the concept of $10n - 1n = 9n$.
- Show how the grids can be used to show the answers to divisions as well as multiplications.
- Children work from Textbook page 59. They use grids to show multiplication and division by 9.
- They then play a Pelmanism game in pairs or small groups, using the Set A cards from PCM 44. They aim to match each multiplication to the correct answer. Children record each calculation and answer as they are found. The child with the most correct pairs is the winner. Support children by showing them how to change the calculations to ×9 multiplications. For example, 55×45 can be changed to $55 \times 5 \times 9$.

Extra help
Children can use a 10×10 dot array to demonstrate the distributive property of multiplication. Children split the array using a horizontal or vertical line. *How many dots are in each section? How many dots in total?* No matter how children split the array, there will always be 100 dots in total.

Further extension
Play the matching game again, this time using the cards from Set B (division).

Be aware

- Some children may need initial support with the distributive property of multiplication. Encourage them to split large numbers into smaller ones to help them to multiply.

Outcomes

- I can multiply a number by 9 by multiplying by 10 and subtracting the number.
- I can divide by 9 in a similar way.
- I can multiply by larger numbers by splitting them up eg. $18 = 2 \times 9$.
- I can quickly double and halve large numbers.

Supporting resources

This game gives times-table practice:
- http://multiplication.com/flashgames/ConeCrazyLevels.htm

Challenge Plan: Year 4

B3: finding differences and relating addition and subtraction; ×9 facts; 8-point compass and turns; angles in degrees

Summary

Y4 ⭐ **B3.3**

Digital roots

Individuals, pairs or groups working independently

Year 4 Challenge Textbook page 60

Year 4 Challenge PCM 45

Calculators (for checking)

Abacus Evolve objectives

- **Y5** Multiply TU × TU using standard written methods
- **Y5** Divide HTU ÷ U using standard written methods (with integer remainder)
- **Y5** Understand the effect of and relationships between the four operations (multiplication and division)

Framework objectives

- **Y5** Refine and use efficient written methods to multiply and divide HTU × U, TU × TU, U·t × U, and HTU ÷ U
- **Y5** Use knowledge of rounding, place value, number facts and inverse operations to estimate and check calculations
- **Y5** Explore patterns, properties and relationships and propose a general statement involving numbers or shapes; identify examples for which the statement is true or false

Teacher notes

Preparation
Photocopy PCM 45 for children who are likely to reach the Extra activity on the Textbook page.

Getting started
Run through the method for finding digital roots. Check that children are confident in using it.

Activity
Children work from Textbook page 60. They read how to calculate digital roots, and are then introduced to a method of checking calculations by using digital roots. Children use digital roots to check the results of multiplications and divisions and discuss how the method works.

Further extension
Each child takes turns to create multiplications and divisions on a calculator. The rest of the group calculate the solutions and use digital roots to check them.

If you have time
Children can use a flip chart to show one of their calculations and go through it with the group.

Information
The digital root of multiples of 9 is always 9. The digital root of any other number is always the same as the remainder when it is divided by 9.

Be aware

- You may need some time to familiarise yourself with the digital root method before doing it with children. The web link below is a useful source of information about digital roots.

Outcomes

- I can explore patterns in numbers, find examples and suggest explanations.
- I can multiply and divide large numbers on paper.
- I can check my answers using digital roots.

Supporting resources

An article about digital roots, with links to other activities that could employ digital roots:
- http://nrich.maths.org/public/viewer.php?obj_id=5524

Challenge Plan: Year 4

B3: finding differences and relating addition and subtraction; ×9 facts; 8-point compass and turns; angles in degrees

Summary

Y4 ☆ B3.4

Bearings

Individuals, pairs or groups working independently

Year 4 Challenge Textbook page 61

Plain paper (preferably A3); rulers; protractors; pairs of compasses; copies of local maps; tracing paper

Abacus Evolve objectives

- Use the eight-point compass directions
- Make and measure clockwise and anticlockwise turns
- Begin to know that angles are measured in degrees
- Recognise the relationship between degrees and right angles

Framework objectives

- Recognise horizontal and vertical lines; use the eight compass points to describe direction; describe and identify the position of a square on a grid of squares
- *Know that angles are measured in degrees and that one whole turn is 360°; draw, compare and order angles less than 180°*
- Suggest a line of enquiry and the strategy needed to follow it; collect, organise and interpret selected information to find answers
- Report solutions to puzzles and problems, giving explanations and reasoning orally and in writing, using diagrams and symbols

Teacher notes

Getting started
Briefly discuss bearings in relation to compass points. Check that children are able to write and use bearings accurately.

Activity
Children work from Textbook page 61. They are introduced to the idea of bearings. Children answer questions, exploring the link between bearings and compass points. They then work on a problem involving the bearings between two coastguard lookout points and a boat. Children use the information on the Textbook page to draw a diagram to represent the situation as accurately as possible on A3 paper, and then solve the problem by taking measurements from their scale drawing.

Extra help
Children can practise working with bearings in the playground. Draw two north lines 10 m apart. Two children (the 'coastguards') stand at two points. Another child (the 'boat') moves to different points in the playground, The 'coastguards' estimate the bearing of the boat.

Further extension
Ask children to explore other positions for the boat, identifying the two bearings that the coastguards would report for each position.

Be aware

- Children may have previously measured angles from a variety of starting points and in both directions (clockwise and anticlockwise). They may need reminding to measure bearings from north only, and always to work clockwise. Drawing in the north line may help.

Outcomes

- I can draw and measure angles using a protractor.
- I can work out the bearing of something by measuring the angle from north.
- I can work out what bearing each compass direction represents.
- I can solve problems by drawing accurate diagrams to scale.

Supporting resources

Try the 'Guess the Random Angle' game on this website:
- http://www.primaryresources.co.uk/maths/mathsE7.htm

B3: finding differences and relating addition and subtraction; ×9 facts; 8-point compass and turns; angles in degrees

Summary

Y4 ✦ B3.5

Hexominoes

A small group working with an adult

2 cm square dot paper

Abacus Evolve objectives

- Make and measure clockwise and anticlockwise turns
- Begin to know that angles are measured in degrees
- Recognise the relationship between degrees and right angles
- Rehearse measuring right-angled turns

Framework objectives

- *Know that angles are measured in degrees and that one whole turn is 360°; compare and order angles less than 180°*
- Use and reflect on some ground rules for dialogue (e.g. making structured, extended contributions, speaking audibly, making meaning explicit and listening actively)

Teacher notes

Activity

- Give each child several sheets of 2 cm square dot paper.
- Remind children about pentominoes and cube nets. *Pentominoes are shapes made by joining five squares. Cube nets are hexominoes – shapes made from six squares. There are lots of these.* (There are 35 hexominoes in total.)
- Ask each child to draw a hexomino in secret on their square dot paper.
- Draw your own secret hexomino. Give children 'robot instructions' for drawing it, such as:
  - Choose a point. Draw a line that goes forward two spaces.
  - Turn clockwise 90 degrees. Move forward one.
  - Turn clockwise 90 degrees. Move forward one.
  - Turn anticlockwise 90 degrees. Move forward four.
  - Turn clockwise 90 degrees. Move forward one.
  - Turn clockwise 90 degrees. Move forward five.
- Check whether children have drawn your hexomino successfully. Discuss any discrepancies.
- Ask children, without revealing their secret shape, to take turns to tell the rest of their group how to draw their own secret hexomino.

Extra help

Children can walk through the 'robot instructions' in the hall or playground.

Further extension

For this extension you will need 1 cm, 2 cm and 4 cm square dot paper. Give children 'robot instructions' for drawing a secret hexomino that is a cube net. They draw it on the 1 cm, 2 cm and 4 cm square dot paper. *How does the different length between dots affect the perimeter in cm? And the area? How many 1 cm by 1 cm by 1 cm cubes could fit into each of these cubes?*

If you have time

Children can use triangle dot paper to find pentiamonds, shapes made from five equilateral triangles.

Be aware

- Some children may need to cut out nets and form cubes practically. Others may need a solid cube.

Outcomes

- I can draw different hexominoes.
- I can give 'robot instructions' for drawing a hexomino.
- I can draw other people's hexominoes by following their 'robot instructions'.

Supporting resources

Use LOGO for further practice with robotic instructions. Online LOGO is available at:
- http://www.mathsnet.net/logo/turtlelogo/index.html

B3: finding differences and relating addition and subtraction; ×9 facts; 8-point compass and turns; angles in degrees

Summary

Y4 ☆ B3.6

Paper-folding angles

Individuals, pairs or groups working independently

Year 4 Challenge Textbook page 62

Year 4 Challenge PCM 46 (optional)

Scissors; rulers; A4 paper in three different colours; sticky tape or glue sticks

Abacus Evolve objectives

- **Y5** Understand and use angle measure in degrees
- **Y5** Rehearse the relationship between degrees and right angles
- **Y5** Recognise acute and obtuse angles in polygons

Framework objectives

- **Y5** Estimate, draw and measure acute and obtuse angles using an angle measurer or protractor to a suitable degree of accuracy; calculate angles in a straight line
- **Y5** Explore patterns, properties and relationships and propose a general statement involving numbers or shapes; identify examples for which the statement is true or false

Teacher notes

Preparation
Photocopy PCM 46, one copy per pair.

Getting started
Use the Textbook page to show children how to fold a 90° angle (a right angle), a 45° angle (half a right angle) and a 135° angle ($1\frac{1}{2}$ right angles) from three different colours of paper.

Activity
Children work from Textbook page 62. They follow the instructions and diagrams on the page to make their own angles. They use sticky tape or glue to secure the folds, then cut out the angles and mark them 1, $\frac{1}{2}$ and $1\frac{1}{2}$. Children draw around their angles to create polygons with these internal angles. They investigate how many different polygons they can make. Children then find the angle total of each polygon (in terms of right angles) and look for any patterns.

Extra help
Children can practise turning through right angles and half right angles. They can record the shape that they are making with each turn.

Further extension
Ask children to make polygons using their three angles as external angles.

If you have time
Children can use circles of paper to make protractors. They find the centre by folding the circle in half, then in half again. They use the $\frac{1}{2}$ right angles that they made to find 45°, 90°, 135°, 180°, 225°, 270°, 315° and 360°. Children who have made $\frac{1}{3}$ right angles can also find 30°, 60°, 120°, 150°, 210°, 240°, 300° and 330°.

Information
It is possible to create one triangle, with angles of 1, $\frac{1}{2}$ and $\frac{1}{2}$ right angles.
Several quadrilaterals are possible (rectangles with four right angles, parallelograms and trapezia with two angles of $1\frac{1}{2}$ and two angles of $\frac{1}{2}$ and so on).
Children can go as far as creating an octagon in which each of the eight angles is $1\frac{1}{2}$ right angles.

Be aware

- The angles need to be accurate for the investigation of shapes to be successful. However, not all children are adept at paper folding and some support may be necessary.

Outcomes

- I can recognise a right angle and I know it is 90°.
- I can work out what different fractions of a right angle are in degrees, such as $\frac{1}{2}$ a right angle.
- I can create different 2D shapes with certain angles.

Supporting resources

Activities on matching properties to shapes can be found at:
- http://www.woodlands-junior.kent.sch.uk/maths/shape.htm Shapes

Challenge Plan: Year 4

C3: coordinates and horizontal and vertical lines; standard units of weight; units of time and calendars; Venn and Carroll diagrams

Summary

Y4 ⭐ C3.1

Roads between towns

Individuals, pairs or groups working independently

Year 4 Challenge Textbook page 63

1 cm square dot paper; 1 cm isometric dot paper; rulers

Abacus Evolve objectives

- **Y5** Recognise parallel and perpendicular lines; use rulers and/or set squares
- **Y5** Recognise properties of rectangles
- **Y5** Classify triangles, using criteria such as equal sides, equal angles, lines of symmetry
- **Y5** Know the meaning of 'diagonal' of a polygon
- **Y5** Measure and draw lines to the nearest millimetre

Framework objectives

- **Y5** *Read and plot coordinates in the first quadrant; recognise parallel and perpendicular lines in grids and shapes; use a set-square and ruler to draw shapes with perpendicular or parallel sides*
- **Y5** Identify, visualise and describe properties of rectangles, triangles, regular polygons and 3D solids; use knowledge of properties to draw 2D shapes and identify and draw nets of 3D shapes
- **Y5** *Draw and measure lines to the nearest millimetre ; measure and calculate the perimeter of regular and irregular polygons; use the formula for the area of a rectangle to calculate its area*
- **Y5** Represent a puzzle or problem by identifying and recording the information or calculations needed to solve it; find possible solutions and confirm them in the context of the problem

Teacher notes

Preparation
Make two triangles. One is a 45° right-angled triangle – half of a 10 cm by 10 cm square. The other is an equilateral triangle, with sides all 10 cm.

Getting started
Encourage children to measure the sides of your two triangles and discuss what they notice.

Activity
Children work from Textbook page 63. They are introduced to a problem in which there are three towns at the corners of a triangle. A new road network is being built to connect the three towns. Children work practically to find the shortest possible road system. They can use isometric dot paper to draw the equilateral triangle and square dot paper to draw the right-angled triangle.
Children then move onto a problem relating to four towns at the corners of a quadrilateral. They can use square dot paper to draw the shape. Encourage children to exchange ideas and compare solutions.

Children can try various strategies using trial and improvement. Strategies with ideas of symmetry will be most successful. In Plan B, for example, the roads must meet at symmetrical angles.

Extra help
Rehearse triangle lines of symmetry. Equilateral triangles have three lines of symmetry crossing in the centre. Isosceles triangles have one line of symmetry.

Be aware

- Children may think the diagonal of a square is the same length as its sides. This activity lets children find out that this is not the case.

Outcomes

- I can investigate all the different possible routes.
- I can use a ruler to measure the length of each route to the nearest millimetre.
- I know the names and properties of 2D shapes.

Supporting resources

Children can play these games to find the shortest route:
- http://nrich.maths.org/public/viewer.php?obj_id=2325

C3: coordinates and horizontal and vertical lines; standard units of weight; units of time and calendars; Venn and Carroll diagrams

Summary

Y4 ⬡ C3.2

Maps

A small group working with an adult

Year 4 Challenge PCM 47

Detailed maps; tracing paper; calculators

Abacus Evolve objectives

- Locate position on a grid, based on labelling the horizontal and vertical lines
- Begin to use the term 'coordinate'
- Use, read and write standard metric units of length: mm, cm, m, km
- Rehearse the relationships between metric units of length
- Begin to multiply integers by 100
- Multiply or divide any integer up to 1000 by 10 and understand the effect
- Use a calculator to carry out one- and two-step calculations, correct mistaken entries and interpret the display correctly in the context of money

Framework objectives

- Recognise horizontal and vertical lines; use the eight compass points to describe direction; describe and identify the position of a square on a grid of squares
- *Choose and use standard metric units and their abbreviations when estimating, measuring and recording length, weight and capacity; know the meaning of 'kilo', 'centi' and 'milli' and, where appropriate, use decimal notation to record measurements (e.g. 1·3 m or 0·6 kg)*
- Multiply and divide numbers to 1000 by 10 and then 100 (whole number answers), understanding the effect; relate to scaling up or down
- Use a calculator to carry out one-step and two-step calculations involving all four operations; recognise negative numbers in the display, correct mistaken entries and interpret the display correctly in the context of money

Teacher notes

Preparation
Photocopy PCM 47, one copy per child, pair or group.
Find some detailed maps of your local area or a place of interest, perhaps related to a current topic. If possible, the maps should use coordinates.

Getting started
Ask children to discuss the maps of the local area or place of interest. Ask questions about the features of the maps and the coordinates system. Discuss the scale of the map. *How far in real life is 1 cm on the map? What would 10 km look like on the map?*
Provide tracing paper and calculators to help with scale calculations.

Activity
Children work from PCM 47. They look at the map and answer questions about the scale and coordinates. Children then write their own scale and coordinates questions about the maps of the local area and the map on the PCM. They exchange questions with others in the group and try to answer them.

If you have time
Children can use the maps of the local area to locate their house and school and find out how far it is from one to the other.

Be aware

- Children may not yet be familiar with converting between units, especially in decimal form. Support may be needed to interpret these calculations.

Outcomes

- I can read coordinates of points on a map.
- I can work out how far distances on a map are in real life.
- I can work out how far a real distance is on a map.

Supporting resources

Print out this Battleships game for children to practise working with coordinates:
- http://www.primaryresources.co.uk/maths/docs/battleships_coordinates.doc

Challenge Plan: Year 4

C3: coordinates and horizontal and vertical lines; standard units of weight; units of time and calendars; Venn and Carroll diagrams

Summary

Y4 ☆ C3.3

Mass and weight

Individuals, pairs or groups working independently

Year 4 Challenge Textbook page 64

Internet access

Abacus Evolve objectives

- Use, read and write standard metric units of weight: kg, g
- Rehearse the relationship between grams and kilograms
- Suggest suitable units and measuring equipment to estimate or measure weight
- Begin to relate fractions to division
- Find fractions of numbers, quantities and shapes

Framework objectives

- *Choose and use standard metric units and their abbreviations when estimating, measuring and recording length, weight and capacity; know the meaning of 'kilo', 'centi' and 'milli' and, where appropriate, use decimal notation to record measurements (e.g. $1.3\,m$ or $0.6\,kg$)*
- Find fractions of numbers, quantities or shapes (e.g. $\frac{1}{5}$ of 30 plums, $\frac{3}{8}$ of a 6 by 4 rectangle)

Teacher notes

Getting started

Write *mass* and *weight* on the board. *What do we mean by mass and weight? Is there a difference between them?* After discussing this, share the definitions of mass and weight on the Textbook page.

Activity

Children work from Textbook page 64. They find the weights of some objects as measured on Earth, and calculate their comparative weights on Mars, the Moon and Saturn's moon, Titan. They record their findings in a table.

If you have time

Children can research minor variations in gravity on the Earth's surface which create tiny differences in weight.

Be aware

- Children will be familiar with measuring in terms of grams and kilograms and referring to this as weight. It is important to point out and make sure they understand that this is technically incorrect as they have been measuring weight with units of mass.

Outcomes

- I understand the difference between weight and mass.
- I can calculate the weight of objects on different planets.
- I can work out fractions of large numbers.

Supporting resources

Children can calculate their weight on other planets:
- http://www.exploratorium.edu/ronh/weight/index.html

Watch this video explaining microgravity ('weightlessness' in space):
- http://www.nasa.gov/audience/foreducators/topnav/materials/listbytype/What_Is_Microgravity.html

Children can research gravity variations with this gravity map of Earth:
- http://www.freerepublic.com/focus/f-news/569855/posts

Challenge Plan: Year 4

C3: coordinates and horizontal and vertical lines; standard units of weight; units of time and calendars; Venn and Carroll diagrams

Summary

Y4 ⬡ C3.4

Half times

Individuals, pairs or groups working independently

Year 4 Challenge Textbook page 65

Analogue clocks or watches; internet access (optional); calculators (optional)

Abacus Evolve objectives

- Use a calendar
- Rehearse time to the nearest minute on 12-hour digital clocks
- Read the time to the nearest minute on analogue clocks
- Use am and pm and the notation 9:53
- Read simple timetables
- Begin to relate fractions to division
- Find fractions of numbers, quantities and shapes

Framework objectives

- Read time to the nearest minute; use am, pm and 12-hour clock notation; choose units of time to measure time intervals; calculate time intervals from clocks and timetables
- Find fractions of numbers, quantities or shapes (e.g. $\frac{1}{5}$ of 30 plums, $\frac{3}{8}$ of a 6 by 4 rectangle)
- Solve one-step and two-step problems involving numbers, money or measures, including time; choose and carry out appropriate calculations, using calculator methods where appropriate

Teacher notes

Getting started

Discuss situations in which it may be useful to know when an activity is half-way through. For example, taking a break half-way through a school day or a long journey.

Remind children that they will need to include am or pm with their times.

Activity

Children work from Textbook page 65. They look at four car journeys and calculate the time at which the family would take a half-time break. Children then extend this idea, finding times at different fractions of the way through the journeys.

Extra help

These problems involve two or more steps. Help children discuss how to break the problems down into each step. Writing each step on a blank card and placing an arrow card between steps, may help children envisage the process.

Further extension

Ask children to design a weekly school timetable based on fractions you give them. For example, $\frac{1}{6}$ of the week is spent on maths; $\frac{1}{10}$ on science; $\frac{1}{12}$ on PE, etc.

Be aware

- These problems involve two or three steps. Children should be supported in dealing with this by continually relating their working out to the initial question.

Outcomes

- I can calculate total journey times by counting on from the start time to the predicted arrival time.
- I can work out halves and doubles of numbers and times.
- I can work out fractions of numbers and times by dividing.
- I can solve problems with several steps.

Supporting resources

Children can solve this train timetable problem:
- http://nrich.maths.org/public/viewer.php?obj_id=958

Challenge Plan: Year 4

C3: coordinates and horizontal and vertical lines; standard units of weight; units of time and calendars; Venn and Carroll diagrams

Summary

Y4 ⬡ C3.5

Carroll and Venn diagrams

A small group working with an adult

Year 4 Challenge Textbook page 66

A3 paper

Abacus Evolve objectives

- Organise and interpret data represented in a Carroll diagram (two criteria)
- Organise and interpret data represented in a Venn diagram (two criteria)

Framework objectives

- *Answer a question by identifying what data to collect; organise, present, analyse and interpret the data in tables, diagrams, tally charts, pictograms and bar charts, using ICT where appropriate*
- Use and reflect on some ground rules for dialogue (e.g. making structured, extended contributions, speaking audibly, making meaning explicit and listening actively)

Teacher notes

Activity
- Introduce the idea of using Venn and Carroll diagrams for sorting numbers and shapes.
- Encourage children to explain what the example diagrams on the Textbook page show. *Which diagram shows the information more clearly? Why?*
- Children work from Textbook page 66. They draw Carroll and Venn diagrams to sort numbers and shapes using the pairs of criteria shown.
- Ask children to invent their own pairs of 'sorting questions'. These may be about shape (e.g. symmetry, parallel lines or right angles) or number (e.g. multiples, factors, square numbers or triangular numbers).

Further extension
Ask children to make a Carroll diagram and add at least 10 numbers to it. They then copy out their diagram but they leave the headings blank. Children then swap diagrams with a partner, and try to find the missing headings.

Extra help
If children are struggling to invent pairs of sorting questions, help them create diagrams for a range of individual questions about a set of numbers of shapes. Then ask them to select two of these and combine them into a two-question diagram.

Be aware

- This activity can also be adapted to suit current class topics or themes if you change the sorting criteria.

Outcomes

- I can sort numbers and shapes using Venn and Carroll diagrams.

Supporting resources

There are several shape sorting games here:
- http://www.woodlands-junior.kent.sch.uk/maths/shape.htm

Challenge Plan: Year 4

C3: coordinates and horizontal and vertical lines; standard units of weight; units of time and calendars; Venn and Carroll diagrams

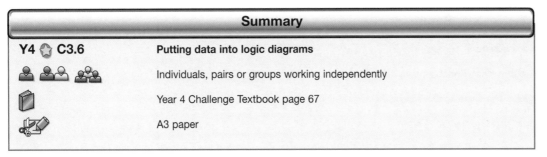

Summary

Y4 ☆ C3.6

Putting data into logic diagrams

Individuals, pairs or groups working independently

Year 4 Challenge Textbook page 67

A3 paper

Abacus Evolve objectives

- Organise and interpret data represented in a Venn diagram (two criteria)
- Organise and interpret data represented in a Carroll diagram (two criteria)

Framework objectives

- *Answer a question by identifying what data to collect; organise, present, analyse and interpret the data in tables, diagrams, tally charts, pictograms and bar charts, using ICT where appropriate*
- Report solutions to puzzles and problems, giving explanations and reasoning orally and in writing, using diagrams and symbols
- Respond appropriately to others in the light of alternative viewpoints

Teacher notes

Getting started
Run through the four steps that children will need to follow, as shown on the Textbook page.

Activity
Children work from Textbook page 67. They decide whether to sort numbers or shapes, and then choose two questions to sort them by. They produce two Venn diagrams and two Carroll diagrams.

Further extension
Children devise their own sets of shapes and numbers, and their own sets of questions for sorting them.

Be aware

- Children may not recognise shapes if they are not in a familiar orientation. Encourage children to imagine rotating the different shapes they see.
- The concept of square numbers is introduced here. Check that children understand and can apply the concept.

Outcomes

- I can sort numbers and shapes into logic diagrams.
- I can recognise multiples of numbers including square numbers.
- I can sort triangles by their angles and side lengths.
- I can recognise right angles in shapes.
- I can describe the properties of different 2D shapes.

Supporting resources

There are several shape sorting games here:
- http://www.woodlands-junior.kent.sch.uk/maths/shape.htm

Summary

Y4 ⭐ D3.1 — **Back numbers**

Groups working independently

Year 4 Challenge Textbook page 68

Plain paper; sticky tape

Abacus Evolve objectives

- Add amounts of money, e.g. £3·26 + £5·85, using standard written methods
- Subtract amounts of money, e.g. £8·40 − £3·76, using standard written method of decomposition
- Add HTU + TU, HTU + HTU using informal written methods
- Subtract HTU − TU, HTU − HTU using informal written method of complementary addition
- Use known number facts and place value to add two 2-digit numbers, adding the tens first
- Use known number facts and place value to subtract one 2-digit number from another, by counting on and back
- Choose and use appropriate operations and appropriate ways of calculating (mental, mental with jottings, pencil and paper) to solve problems

Framework objectives

- Refine and use efficient written methods to add and subtract 2-digit and 3-digit whole numbers and £·p
- *Add or subtract mentally pairs of two-digit whole numbers (e.g. 47 + 58, 91 − 35)*
- Solve one-step and two-step problems involving numbers, money or measures, including time; choose and carry out appropriate calculations, using calculator methods where appropriate
- Represent a puzzle or problem using number sentences, statements or diagrams; use these to solve the problem; present and interpret the solution in the context of the problem
- Respond appropriately to others in the light of alternative viewpoints

Teacher notes

Preparation
Prepare a few pieces of paper with numbers or money values written on, for children to play the 'back numbers' game.

Getting started
Discuss the game that the children are playing on the Textbook page. Each child has a number stuck to their back. They do not know what it is. They each say the total of the numbers they can see on the other two children's backs. Using this information, each child works out the number on their own back.
Check that children know how to use known number facts to find the hidden numbers.

Activity
Children work from Textbook page 68. They work out the numbers on each child's back and look for patterns. Children then play the game themselves, securing numbers to their backs with sticky tape. They then solve similar problems involving three or four children playing the game with numbers or amounts of money.

Extra help
Prepare three 1-digit number cards and write down the three totals that can be found by adding two of the numbers each time. For example, 2, 5, 8: 2 + 5 = 7, 2 + 8 = 10, 5 + 8 = 13. Ask children to say which two digit cards give each total.

Further extension
Children think of three numbers, one for their own back and one each for two other children. They say which three totals would be generated. Children then imagine that their back number increases or decreases by 5, and explore the effect that has on the totals.

Be aware

- Children may initially need some support to avoid just guessing randomly. The activity requires logical deduction, such as:
  If A + B = 80 and A + C = 120 then C must be 40 more than B.
  If necessary, point out a strategy to get children started.

Outcomes

- I can add and subtract 2-digit numbers in my head.
- I can use pen and paper to add and subtract more difficult numbers and amounts of money.
- I can find hidden numbers from known number facts.

Supporting resources

Try this 'Number puzzle' worksheet:
- http://www.beam.co.uk/uploads/mompdf/Number%20puzzle.pdf

Summary

Y4 ☆ D3.2

Subtraction options

A small group working with an adult

Year 4 Challenge Textbook page 69

Digit cards (optional)

Abacus Evolve objectives

- Subtract amounts of money, e.g. £8·40 − £3·76, using standard written method of decomposition
- Use known number facts and place value to subtract one 2-digit number from another, by counting on and back
- Choose and use appropriate operations and appropriate ways of calculating (mental, mental with jottings, pencil and paper) to solve problems

Framework objectives

- Refine and use efficient written methods to add and subtract 2-digit and 3-digit whole numbers and £·p
- *Add or subtract mentally pairs of two-digit whole numbers (e.g. 47 + 58, 91 − 35)*
- Solve one-step and two-step problems involving numbers, money or measures, including time; choose and carry out appropriate calculations, using calculator methods where appropriate
- Use and reflect on some ground rules for dialogue (e.g. making structured, extended contributions, speaking audibly, making meaning explicit and listening actively)

Teacher notes

Activity

- Introduce the spider diagram on the Textbook page. *How do we get to each new calculation at the end of each leg? Which new calculation do you find easiest to calculate? Why?*
- Draw a spider diagram with *319 − 122* in the centre. *What can we write at the end of each leg?* Children suggest new calculations to fill as many of the legs as possible. *Which calculation is easiest? Why?*
- Children work from Textbook page 69. Look together at the questions. Children draw their own spider diagram for each calculation. For each diagram ask: *Which is your easiest calculation? Can you now do it easily in your head?* Encourage children to solve each subtraction using the calculation they find the easiest (mentally where possible).
- Children should then check their answers using a method of their choice.

If you have time

Children can make their own spider diagram. They exchange it with a partner who decides which calculation they will use to find the answer and explain why they chose it.

Be aware

- Children need to understand that subtraction answers remain the same as long as both numbers are adjusted by the same amount. This should become clear to children after they have worked through a few examples. However, children should be reminded that this is not the case with addition, e.g. 121 − 20 gives the same answer as 131 − 30, but 121 + 20 does not give the same answer as 131 + 30.

Outcomes

- I can find different subtractions that give the same answer.
- I can use this to help me add and subtract numbers and amounts of money in my head.
- I can work out what to add to or subtract from different numbers to make them up to the nearest 10 or 100.
- I can check my answers using the inverse calculation or digital roots.

Supporting resources

Use these subtraction bingo cards or create your own:
- http://www.bingocardscreator.com/bingo_math_subtract_3.php

D3: adding money amounts; subtracting money amounts; ×7 multiplication and division facts; multiplying TU by U

Summary

Y4 ⭐ D3.3

Half-price sale

Individuals, pairs or groups working independently

Year 4 Challenge Textbook page 70

Year 4 Challenge PCM 48

Abacus Evolve objectives

- **Y5** Use known number facts and place value for mental addition and subtraction of decimals
- **Y5** Subtract one decimal number from another, both with one or both with two decimal places, using informal and standard written methods
- **Y5** Derive doubles of integers up to 100 and 2-digit decimals and their corresponding halves
- **Y5** Relate fractions to division
- **Y5** Use division to find fractions, including tenths and hundredths of numbers and quantities

Framework objectives

- **Y5** *Use efficient written methods to add and subtract whole numbers and decimals with up to two places*
- **Y5** *Use knowledge of place value and addition and subtraction of 2-digit numbers to derive sums and differences, doubles and halves of decimals (e.g. 6·5 + 2·7, 6·5 − 2·7, halve 5·6, double 0·34)*
- **Y5** *Find fractions using division (e.g. $\frac{1}{100}$ of 5 kg), and percentages of numbers and quantities (e.g. 10%, 5% and 15% of £80)*
- **Y5** *Solve one-step and two-step problems involving whole numbers and decimals and all four operations, choosing and using appropriate calculation strategies, including calculator use*

Teacher notes

Getting started
Look together at the items on Textbook page 70. Discuss the concept of price reductions and decide together which items are exactly half price, which items cost a little more than half price and which items cost a little less than half price.

Activity
Children work from PCM 48. The PCM shows a flyer for a sale. Items of clothing are labelled with both their original price and the sale price. Children sort the items according to the fraction or percentage they are discounted by (a little more than 50% off, exactly half price, a little less than 50% off, a little more than $\frac{1}{3}$ off, exactly $\frac{1}{3}$ off, or a little less than $\frac{1}{3}$ off).

Extra help
An item costs £10. *What price would it be if there was 50% off?* Rehearse finding half of the amount and subtracting it from the original price. (£5.) *What price would be just over 50% off?* (Around £4.) *What price would be just under 50% off?* (Around £6.)

Further extension
Give children some original prices and ask them to calculate the sale prices with given percentage or fraction reductions.
Ask pupils to research common ways of wording sale prices, e.g. *Buy three for the price of two* or *Buy one, get one free.*

Be aware

- Children that move on to the 'Extra' activity may find that exploring original prices from sale prices is more challenging. Encourage discussion and give support where necessary.

Outcomes

- I can halve amounts of money.
- I can begin to work out fractions of numbers by dividing them by the denominator of the fraction.

Supporting resources

A money fractions game:
- http://nrich.maths.org/public/viewer.php?obj_id=2730

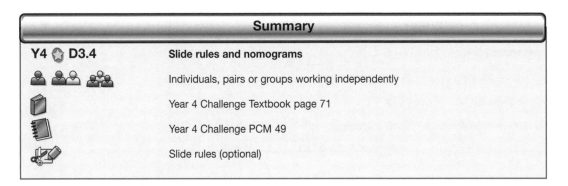

Challenge Plan: Year 4

D3: adding money amounts; subtracting money amounts; ×7 multiplication and division facts; multiplying TU by U

Summary

Y4 ✪ D3.4

Slide rules and nomograms

Individuals, pairs or groups working independently

Year 4 Challenge Textbook page 71

Year 4 Challenge PCM 49

Slide rules (optional)

Abacus Evolve objectives

- Know by heart the multiplication facts for the 2, 3, 4, 5 and 10 times tables
- Derive division facts corresponding to the 2, 3, 4, 5 and 10 times tables
- Know the multiplication facts for the 6 times table, and the corresponding division facts
- Begin to know the multiplication facts for the 8 times table, and the corresponding division facts
- Begin to know the multiplication facts for the 9 times table, and the corresponding division facts
- Begin to know the multiplication facts for the 7 times table, and the corresponding division facts

Framework objectives

- *Derive and recall multiplication facts up to 10 × 10, the corresponding division facts and multiples of numbers to 10 up to the tenth multiple*
- Identify and use patterns, relationships and properties of numbers or shapes; investigate a statement involving numbers and test it with examples

Teacher notes

Preparation
Photocopy PCM 49, one copy per child.

Getting started
Look together at the photograph of the slide rule on the Textbook page. Discuss with children how it can be used to multiply or divide by 2. If possible, show children some real slide rules.

Activity
Children work from Textbook page 71. They read about John Napier's work on logarithms and slide rules, then explore the patterns in how the numbers on the slide rule scale are placed.
Children then move on to use the nomogram on PCM 49 to solve multiplications and divisions.

If you have time
Provide a 3-digit logarithms table. Ask children to work together to check simple multiplication and division facts, using the table.

Be aware

- Children are unlikely to know how a slide rule works and should be encouraged to discuss it, sharing ideas.

Outcomes

- I can see how a slide rule is used to multiply and divide.
- I can use a nomogram to multiply and divide.

Supporting resources

Look here for more information about slide rules and how to use them:
- http://www.sliderules.clara.net/a-to-z/background.htm
A virtual slide rule:
- http://www.engcom.net/index.php?option=com_sliderule&Itemid=73

Summary

Y4 ☆ D3.5

Investigating patterns from 7s

Individuals, pairs or groups working independently

Year 4 Challenge Textbook page 72

Lists of times tables from ×2 to ×10; calculators

Abacus Evolve objectives

- Begin to know the multiplication facts for the 7 times table, and the corresponding division facts
- Know by heart the multiplication facts for the 2, 3, 4, 5 and 10 times tables
- Begin to relate fractions to division
- Recognise and explain patterns and relationships, generalise and predict
- Make and investigate a general statement about familiar numbers or shapes by finding examples that satisfy it (number)

Framework objectives

- *Derive and recall multiplication facts up to 10 × 10, the corresponding division facts and multiples of numbers to 10 up to the tenth multiple*
- Identify and use patterns, relationships and properties of numbers or shapes; investigate a statement involving numbers and test it with examples
- Report solutions to puzzles and problems, giving explanations and reasoning orally and in writing, using diagrams and symbols

Teacher notes

Getting started
Display the times-tables from ×2 to ×10. Ask children to suggest 'families' of related tables. (2, 4 and 8 are related; 3, 6 and 9 are related; 2, 5 and 10 are related.) Focus on the ×7 table as being unusual because it isn't related to any other tables.

Activity
Children work from Textbook page 72. They investigate the pattern of units digits in the 7 times-table and find other times-table units digit patterns with the same property (×1 and ×9).
Children then calculate how many 7s there are in 10, 100, 1000, ... up to 1 000 000. They record the pattern they see in their answers.
Children then explore sevenths as decimals. They relate the pattern they find to the previous pattern and extend their exploration to improper fractions with a denominator of 7.

Further extension
Children could explore patterns related to multiples of 7; for example, unit patterns in the 21 times-table, or how fourteenths are written as decimals.

If you have time
Children can explore the effects of multiplying by 7, focussing on the units digit. For example $7 \times 4 = 28$, $7 \times 14 = 98$, $7 \times 24 = 168$. (In this case the units digit changes from 4 to 8.)

Be aware

- Children may not yet have consolidated the link between fractions, division and the corresponding decimal, e.g. $\frac{1}{7} = 1 \div 7$. Support this with imagery, such as dividing an array of 7 lots of any number into seven pieces.

Outcomes

- I know the 7 times-table.
- I can divide large numbers by 7 and find patterns in the answers.
- I can use my calculator to work out fractions as decimals.
- I can find and investigate patterns in numbers and calculations.

Summary

Y4 ✦ D3.6	**Multiplying odd and even numbers**
	A small group working with an adult
	Year 4 Challenge PCM 50
	Thin card

Abacus Evolve objectives

- **Y5** Multiply TU × TU using standard written methods
- **Y5** Rehearse dividing TU ÷ U using informal written methods
- **Y5** Know by heart all multiplication facts up to 10 × 10
- **Y5** Use knowledge of sums or differences of odd/even numbers to check calculations

Framework objectives

- **Y5** Refine and use efficient written methods to multiply and divide HTU × U, TU × TU, U·t × U, and HTU ÷ U
- **Y5** Recall quickly multiplication facts up to 10 × 10, use to multiply pairs of multiples of 10 and 100 and derive quickly corresponding division facts
- **Y5** Use knowledge of rounding, place value, number facts and inverse operations to estimate and check calculations
- **Y5** Understand different ways to take the lead and support others in a group

Teacher notes

Preparation
Photocopy PCM 50 onto thin card, one copy per pair. Cut out the cards.

Activity
- Split the cards in set A into even numbers and odd numbers. Demonstrate taking a card from each pile and multiplying the numbers together. For example, for 3 × 16, model starting from 3 × 8 and doubling the answer.
- Children take turns to draw a card from each pile and decide which strategy they will use to multiply the numbers.
- Ask children to get into pairs. Give each pair the cards from set B. They remove the blank cards and split the number cards into even numbers and odd numbers. Children take turns to draw a card from each pile. Pairs develop strategies for multiplying the numbers. They write six products on their blank cards.
- Bring the group back together. Spread out all the cards from set B, and ask each pair to add their product cards to the collection. Children work as a group to work out which pair of numbers was multiplied to make each product. Encourage children to use their knowledge of the products of odd and even numbers.

If you have time
Children can make their own set A cards and explore possible products.

Be aware

- If children are struggling to find strategies, they should be encouraged to split large numbers into a pair of simpler numbers before multiplying.
- Some children may confuse the inverse relationship between multiplication and division facts, for example, thinking that because 3 × 5 = 15, 5 ÷ 15 = 3.

Outcomes

- I can multiply difficult numbers by splitting them into simpler numbers.
- I can estimate multiplications by rounding numbers, and use my estimates to check my answers.
- I can use odd and even number facts to check my answers.

Challenge Plan: Year 4

E3: multiply TU by U; divide TU by U; find fractions of numbers, quantities and shapes; equivalence between fractions and decimals

Summary

Y4 ⭐ E3.1 **Factor record-breakers**

A small group working with an adult

Year 4 Challenge Textbook page 73

Year 4 Challenge PCM 51

Coloured pencils; calculators (optional)

Abacus Evolve objectives

- **Y5** Know by heart all multiplication facts up to 10 × 10
- **Y5** Derive quickly division facts corresponding to multiplication facts up to 10 × 10
- **Y5** Find all the pairs of factors of any number up to 100
- **Y5** Know and apply tests of divisibility by 2, 4, 5, 10 and 100
- **Y5** Recognise and explain patterns and relationships, generalise and predict

Framework objectives

- **Y5** Recall quickly multiplication facts up to 10 × 10, use to multiply pairs of multiples of 10 and 100 and derive quickly corresponding division facts
- **Y5** Identify pairs of factors of 2-digit whole numbers and find common multiples (e.g. for 6 and 9)
- **Y5** Explore patterns, properties and relationships and propose a general statement involving numbers or shapes; identify examples for which the statement is true or false

Teacher notes

Preparation
Photocopy PCM 51, one copy per child, pair or group.

Activity
- Introduce the idea of factors by looking together at the factor tables on the Textbook page. *What are the factors of 15?* (1, 3, 5, 15). Model using a factor table to find all the factors of 15.
- Children work from Textbook page 73. They draw factor tables for the numbers 1 to 15.
- *Some numbers are factor record-breakers! The number 1 is a record-breaker because it is the first number with one factor. The number 2 is a record breaker because it is the first number with two factors. Look at your factor tables. What are the next three record breakers?* (4, 6 and 12)
- Children find the factor record-breakers up to 100 and circle them on PCM 51.
- They then colour code the 1–120 number square to show different numbers of factors.
- *Can you see any patterns?*

Information
The factor record-breakers up to 100 are 1, 2, 4, 6, 12, 24, 36, 48, 60. The next record-breaker after 100 is 120.

Be aware

- Children will encounter prime numbers in this activity and may discuss what they notice about them. Children should not have a problem with this level of engagement with prime numbers.

Outcomes

- I can use my knowledge of times-tables to help me find factors of numbers up to 100.
- I can find and explore number patterns.

Supporting resources

Here are some interactive games about factors and multiples:
- http://nrich.maths.org/public/viewer.php?obj_id=5468
- http://www.hughchou.org/hugh/grid_game.cgi

Challenge Plan: Year 4

E3: multiply TU by U; divide TU by U; find fractions of numbers, quantities and shapes; equivalence between fractions and decimals

Summary

Y4 ☆ E3.2

Multiplication patterns

Individuals, pairs or groups working independently

Year 4 Challenge Textbook page 74

Calculators

Abacus Evolve objectives

- Multiply TU × U using standard written methods
- Understand multiplication as repeated addition
- Use known number facts and place value to multiply or divide mentally
- Use a calculator to carry out one- and two-step calculations, correct mistaken entries and interpret the display correctly in the context of money
- Make and investigate a general statement about familiar numbers or shapes by finding examples that satisfy it (number)

Framework objectives

- *Develop and use written methods to record, support and explain multiplication and division of two-digit numbers by a one-digit number, including division with remainders (e.g. 15 × 9, 98 ÷ 6)*
- Use a calculator to carry out one-step and two-step calculations involving all four operations; recognise negative numbers in the display, correct mistaken entries and interpret the display correctly in the context of money
- Identify and use patterns, relationships and properties of numbers or shapes; investigate a statement involving numbers and test it with examples

Teacher notes

Getting started

We are going to try doing multiplications without actually multiplying.
We will look for patterns to help us.

$9 \times 12 = 108$ $\quad$ $9 \times 45 =$
$9 \times 23 = 207$ $\quad$ $9 \times 56 =$
$9 \times 34 = 306$ $\quad$ $9 \times 67 =$

Try to guess the next few answers. ($9 \times 45 = 405$, $9 \times 56 = 504$, $9 \times 67 = 603$)

Activity

Children work from Textbook page 74. They extend the pattern to find answers up to 9×89.

Children then find the patterns for these sequences and continue them until they can go no further:

9×123, 9×234, 9×345, ...
9×11, 19×21, 29×31, ...
20×20, 19×21, 18×22, ...

For all four sequences children check their answers with a calculator, then describe how long the patterns last and what happens when they end.

Children then identify the patterns for 1×1089, 2×1089, 3×1089, ... and 1×9109, 2×9109, 3×9109, ... They continue the patterns up to $10 \times$ ...

Be aware

- Children may not yet be familiar with multiplying a 2-digit number by a 2-digit number. They should be able to identify a pattern for answering these calculations, rather than using standard methods.

Outcomes

- I can investigate patterns in sequences of multiplications.
- I can use a calculator to check my answers.

E3: multiply TU by U; divide TU by U; find fractions of numbers, quantities and shapes; equivalence between fractions and decimals

Summary

Y4 ☆ E3.3

Napier's bones

Individuals, pairs or groups working independently

Year 4 Challenge Textbook page 75

Year 4 Challenge PCM 52

Thin card; calculators

Abacus Evolve objectives

- Multiply TU × U using standard written methods
- Multiply TU × U using informal written methods: grid method
- Begin to multiply integers by 100
- Multiply or divide any integer up to 1000 by 10 and understand the effect
- Use known number facts and place value to multiply or divide mentally

Framework objectives

- *Develop and use written methods to record, support and explain multiplication and division of two-digit numbers by a one-digit number, including division with remainders (e.g. 15 × 9, 98 ÷ 6)*
- Multiply and divide numbers to 1000 by 10 and then 100 (whole number answers), understanding the effect; relate to scaling up or down

Teacher notes

Preparation
Photocopy PCM 52 onto thin card, one copy per child, pair or group. Cut out the bones.
Familiarise yourself with using Napier's bones to multiply.

Getting started
Read together about Napier's bones on the Textbook page. Check that children understand the example.
Show them how to use the bones to solve a multiplication. For example, to work out 3 × 25, lay the '2' bone and the '5' bone side by side, and place the index bone to the left of them. Read across from the number 3, and explain how much the number above and below the diagonal lines are worth. Add them up: 60 + 10 + 5 = 75.

Activity
Children work from Textbook page 75. They use Napier's bones from PCM 52 to solve six U × TU calculations. They then try using the bones to solve a U × HTU calculation and generate the 215 times table up to 9 × 215.

Further extension
Children scale the Textbook page calculations down by ÷10 or ÷100 and use the bones to multiply decimals.

If you have time
Children can explore the use of Napier bones with division.

Information
This method relates to current partitioning methods, but 'loses' the place value meaning of each digit.
Napier's bones can also be used for division. The content of each bone is the dividend. The heading of each bone is the divisor and the index bone is the quotient.

Be aware

- Using Napier's bones requires confidence in understanding and using place value. Children may encounter some errors in this area but should be able to correct themselves with support.

Outcomes

- I can multiply large numbers using Napier's bones.
- I understand what each digit in a large number represents.
- I can multiply numbers by 10 and 100 and understand what happens when I do this.

Supporting resources

Children can use these interactive Napier's bones:
- http://gwydir.demon.co.uk/jo/numbers/machine/napier.htm interact
Find out more about Gelosia multiplication at:
- http://homepage.mac.com/shelleywalsh/MathArt/GelosiaMultiply.html

Challenge Plan: Year 4

E3: multiply TU by U; divide TU by U; find fractions of numbers, quantities and shapes; equivalence between fractions and decimals

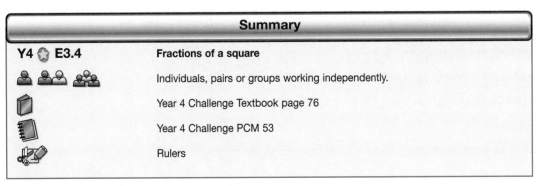

Summary

Y4 ☆ E3.4

Fractions of a square

Individuals, pairs or groups working independently.

Year 4 Challenge Textbook page 76

Year 4 Challenge PCM 53

Rulers

Abacus Evolve objectives

- Find fractions of numbers, quantities and shapes
- Find quarters by halving halves
- Recognise simple fractions that are several parts of a whole
- Recognise mixed numbers
- Recognise the equivalence of simple fractions
- Rehearse the concept of line symmetry

Framework objectives

- Find fractions of numbers, quantities or shapes (e.g. $\frac{1}{5}$ of 30 plums, $\frac{3}{8}$ of a 6 by 4 rectangle)
- Use diagrams to identify equivalent fractions (e.g. $\frac{6}{8}$ and $\frac{3}{4}$, or $\frac{70}{100}$ and $\frac{7}{10}$); interpret mixed numbers and position them on a number line (e.g. $3\frac{1}{2}$)
- Report solutions to puzzles and problems, giving explanations and reasoning orally and in writing, using diagrams and symbols

Teacher notes

Preparation
Photocopy PCM 53, one copy per child, pair or group.

Getting started
Look together at the example tiles on the Textbook page. Make sure children understand how to design a tile.

Activity
Children work from Textbook page 76. They explore all the possible ways to divide a square tile using two lines. Hints are provided to different strategies. Some lines cross within the square, some lines meet at point, some lines do not meet.
There are 20 different patterns that can be made. There are four different line lengths: corner to corner, corner to mid-point, mid-point to opposite mid-point and mid-point to adjacent mid-point.
Each whole square is made of four small squares, or eight small triangles. Children investigate the fractions they have constructed.

Extra help
Children can initially make patterns where lines do not cross. It is easier to find fractions of these shapes and there are only three fractions to find.

Further extension
Children cut one set of tiles into cards and share them out. Children take turns to play a card. One side of the tile must match one side of the tile played before. A score is found by adding the value of the two tile segments that have been joined, e.g. $1\frac{1}{2} + 1\frac{1}{2} = 3$. The child with the highest score when all cards have been played is the winner.

If you have time
Give each child a set of tile cards. They each turn over their top card. The fraction value of the largest segment on each tile is compared and the largest wins. Where there is a tie, the second largest segment is compared.

Be aware

- Children may make some designs that are rotations or reflections of each other. They may need prompting to identify and disregard these.

Outcomes

- I can investigate ways to divide up a square tile.
- I can work out what fractions I have created.
- I can recognise and write mixed numbers.

Supporting resources

Children can try these fraction games:
- http://www.numbernut.com/advanced/activities/fraction_4card_groups.shtml
- http://www.visualfractions.com/Games.htm

Challenge Plan: Year 4

E3: multiply TU by U; divide TU by U; find fractions of numbers, quantities and shapes; equivalence between fractions and decimals

Summary

Y4 ⭐ E3.5

Fractions and decimals link cards

A small group working with an adult

Year 4 Challenge PCM 54

Thin card

Abacus Evolve objectives

- **Y5** Relate fractions to division
- **Y5** Use division to find fractions, including tenths and hundredths of numbers and quantities
- **Y5** Use fraction notation, including mixed numbers, and the vocabulary 'numerator' and 'denominator'
- **Y5** Change an improper fraction to a mixed number, and vice versa
- **Y5** Recognise equivalence between fractions and decimals

Framework objectives

- **Y5** Find fractions using division (e.g. $\frac{1}{100}$ of 5 kg), and percentages of numbers and quantities (e.g. 10%, 5% and 15% of £80)
- **Y5** Express a smaller whole number as a fraction of a larger one (e.g. recognise that 5 out of 8 is $\frac{5}{8}$); find equivalent fractions (e.g. $\frac{7}{10} = \frac{14}{20}$, or $\frac{19}{10} = 1\frac{9}{10}$); relate fractions to their decimal representations
- **Y5** Understand different ways to take the lead and support others in a group

Teacher notes

Preparation
Photocopy PCM 54 onto thin card, one copy per pair or group. Cut out the cards.

Activity
Practise the connections between fractions and decimals. *What is $\frac{1}{2}$ as a decimal? How many quarters is that? How many tenths? What is $\frac{1}{5}$ as a decimal? How many tenths is that? What is $\frac{2}{5}$ as a decimal?*
Give each pair or group a set of six linking cards from PCM 54. (The sets are labelled A, B, C and D.) The solution to each question is on another card. Children solve each question to link the cards into a chain.
As they complete one chain, give them another set of cards, until they have completed all four chains.
Bring the group together. Shuffle all 24 cards together and deal them out. Ask a child whose card has the answer 2·5 written on it to start. They read out the question on their card. Players take turns to play the next card or 'pass', until one player has no cards left and is the winner.

Extra help
Children can use a doubling strategy to solve some of the cards. For example, $\frac{1}{3}$ of 4·5. Instead find $\frac{1}{3}$ of 9 (3), then halve the answer (1·5).

If you have time
Play the game again, but faster. Allow a 'play when you can go' rule rather than asking children to take turns.

Information
In a set of six cards any card may be placed first in the chain, as they form a loop of six cards.

Be aware

- Check that children understand what place value the places after the decimal point represent. This will help them when converting from a fraction to a decimal.

Outcomes

- I can convert simple fractions into decimals.
- I can convert improper fractions to mixed numbers.
- I can find fractions of numbers by dividing.
- I know what the places are after the decimal point.

Supporting resources

This is a game matching fractions and decimals:
- http://www.bbc.co.uk/skillswise/numbers/fractiondecimalpercentage/comparing/fractionsdecimals/game.shtml

Challenge Plan: Year 4

E3: multiply TU by U; divide TU by U; find fractions of numbers, quantities and shapes; equivalence between fractions and decimals

Summary

Y4 ⭐ E3.6   **Missing fractions and decimals**

Individuals, pairs or groups working independently

Year 4 Challenge Textbook page 77

Digit cards 0–9; calculators

Abacus Evolve objectives

- Use decimal notation for tenths
- Recognise the equivalence between the decimal and fraction forms of halves and tenths
- Recognise the equivalence between the decimal and fraction forms of halves and quarters
- Begin to relate fractions to division
- Find fractions of numbers, quantities and shapes

Framework objectives

- Recognise the equivalence between decimal and fraction forms of one half, quarters, tenths and hundredths
- Find fractions of numbers, quantities or shapes (e.g. $\frac{1}{5}$ of 30 plums, $\frac{3}{8}$ of a 6 by 4 rectangle)
- Suggest a line of enquiry and the strategy needed to follow it; collect, organise and interpret selected information to find answers

Teacher notes

Getting started
Give each child, pair or group a set of digit cards 0–9.
Ask children to use their digit cards to recreate the first question on the Textbook page. Check that children understand what each element of the calculation represents and are able to solve it.

Activity
Children work from Textbook page 77. They answer missing number questions involving fractions.
Children then work back from a whole-number answer to find what the fraction problem could have been.
They then solve missing-number problems involving decimals with one decimal place.

Extra help
Children can start by finding $\frac{1}{2}$, $\frac{1}{3}$ and $\frac{1}{4}$ of 2-digit numbers, then move on when their confidence has grown.

Further extension
Write ☐☐ ÷ ☐ = 8·4. *The missing digits are 2, 4 and 5. What is the calculation?* Children use a calculator to investigate. *What other division calculations can you make with these three digits? What is the answer each time? Is it a decimal, a whole number or a mixed number?*

Be aware

- If children still find equivalent fractions difficult, support them with diagrams and imagery, such as a fraction/decimal wall.

Outcomes

- I can find fractions of numbers by dividing them into the correct number of parts.
- I can find the decimal equivalents of some fractions.
- I can add decimals with one decimal place.
- I can work backwards from an answer and investigate what the question might have been.

Year 4 Autumn Assessment Activity

Egyptian fractions

Assessment Foci: L4 Using and applying mathematics (Problem solving; Communicating; Reasoning); L4 Number (Fractions, decimals, percentages and ratio)

Resources: PCMs A–E; counters; square dot paper; calculators

Lesson 1 – preparation – 1 hour

Part 1 – introduction – 20 minutes

A unit fraction is a fraction with a numerator of 1, for example $\frac{1}{5}$. Ancient Egyptian mathematicians used only unit fractions for numbers less than 1. This is because their way of indicating a fraction was to just draw a bar across the number that represented the denominator. They didn't write a numerator. This is why our fractions have a bar between the two numbers.

Give children PCM A. They investigate the numbers that are unit fractions of 12, by sharing 12 counters into equal groups. Children then add pairs of fractions to give fractions of 12. They simplify the answers if possible.

To extend: ask children to find all the unit fractions of 24 by sharing 24 counters into equal groups. Encourage children to use known multiplication facts to help them find the unit fractions. For example, if they know that $3 \times 8 = 24$, this should lead them to $\frac{1}{3}$ of $24 = 8$, and $\frac{1}{8}$ of $24 = 3$. Once children have listed all the unit fractions, ask them to add pairs or threes of unit fractions, giving the answers in 24ths and simplifying where possible.

Part 2 – development – 30 minutes

Bring the group back together for a 5-minute discussion comparing their work so far.

Give children PCM B. Read together the story of Hamadi's camels, and the solution offered by Sharifa. Ask children to discuss why the extra camel allowed each child to receive their allocated fraction of camels, and Sharifa's camel was no longer needed.

Ask children to think of an idea for a similar story, involving a problem with fractions and a puzzling solution. They could illustrate it with drawings or diagrams. If they need a hint, their story could involve trying to divide one of these numbers: 11, 17, 19, 23, 27, 35 or 41.

Part 3 – plenary – 10 minutes

Give each child a chance to tell their fraction story to the group.

Lesson 2 – investigation – 1 hour

Part 1 – introduction – 10 minutes

Remind children that the ancient Egyptians only used unit fractions. *How do you think they would have shown a fraction like two-fifths?* Give children PCMs C and D, and lots of counters. *They would split a fraction like this into unit fractions. They would always start with the largest unit fraction possible.*

Take children through the example on PCM C, asking them to use counters and the fraction number lines on PCM D, and work through it in pairs.

How could you split two-quarters into unit fractions? Encourage children to recognise that a fraction with a numerator of 2 and an even denominator can be reduced to a unit fraction. ($\frac{2}{4} = \frac{1}{2}$)

Explain to children that they are going to split other fractions with a numerator of 2 into unit fractions, and look for patterns. If they have time, they will move on to fractions with a numerator of 3. Ask them to record some brief initial ideas and conjectures about the investigation. Encourage them to plan how they will record their work. Make counters, square dot paper and calculators available.

Part 2 – investigation – 30 minutes

Children work individually to develop their lines of investigation, recording their journey and any findings.

Part 3 – conclusions – 20 minutes

Children write a final report of their investigation, showing their journey and findings along the way, with any conclusions or fresh ideas.

Ask children to complete the self-assessment sheet on PCM E.

Egyptian fractions

Objectives

These are the objectives that could be met by children doing this Assessment Activity.

Strand	Abacus Evolve objectives	Framework objectives
Using and applying mathematics	**Y4** Recognise and explain patterns and relationships, generalise and predict **Y4** Make and investigate a general statement about familiar numbers or shapes by finding examples that satisfy it (number)	**Y4** Represent a puzzle or problem using number sentences, statements or diagrams; use these to solve the problem; present and interpret the solution in the context of the problem **Y4** Suggest a line of enquiry and the strategy needed to follow it; collect, organise and interpret selected information to find answers **Y4** Identify and use patterns, relationships and properties of numbers or shapes; investigate a statement involving numbers and test it with examples **Y4** Report solutions to puzzles and problems, giving explanations and reasoning orally and in writing, using diagrams and symbols
Counting and understanding number	**Y4** Recognise simple fractions that are several parts of a whole **Y4** Recognise the equivalence of simple fractions **Y4** Compare and order fractions **Y4** Locate fractions on a number line **Y5** Use fraction notation, including mixed numbers, and the vocabulary 'numerator' and 'denominator' **Y5** Recognise when two simple fractions are equivalent **Y5** Order fractions and position them on a number line	**Y4** *Use diagrams to identify equivalent fractions (e.g. $\frac{6}{8}$ and $\frac{3}{4}$, or $\frac{70}{100}$ and $\frac{7}{10}$; interpret mixed numbers and position them on a number line, e.g. $3\frac{1}{2}$)* **Y5** Express a smaller whole number as a fraction of a larger one (e.g. recognise that 5 out of 8 is $\frac{5}{8}$); find equivalent fractions (e.g. $\frac{7}{10} = \frac{14}{20}$, or $\frac{19}{10} = 1\frac{9}{10}$); relate fractions to their decimal representations
Calculating	**Y4** Find fractions of numbers, quantities and shapes	**Y4** Find fractions of numbers, quantities or shapes (e.g. $\frac{1}{5}$ of 30 plums, $\frac{3}{8}$ of a 6 by 4 rectangle)

Egyptian fractions

Answers

Note: these answers are not exhaustive.

Preparation

Part 1 – introduction

PCM A:

$\frac{1}{3}$ of 12 = 4
$\frac{1}{4}$ of 12 = 3
$\frac{1}{2}$ of 12 = 6
$\frac{1}{6}$ of 12 = 2
$\frac{1}{12}$ of 12 = 1

$\frac{1}{2} + \frac{1}{3} = \frac{10}{12} = \frac{5}{6}$
$\frac{1}{3} + \frac{1}{12} = \frac{5}{12}$
$\frac{1}{4} + \frac{1}{6} = \frac{5}{12}$
$\frac{1}{6} + \frac{1}{6} = \frac{8}{12} = \frac{2}{3}$
etc.

Unit fractions of 24:

$\frac{1}{2}$ of 24 = 12
$\frac{1}{3}$ of 24 = 8
$\frac{1}{4}$ of 24 = 6
$\frac{1}{6}$ of 24 = 4
$\frac{1}{8}$ of 24 = 3
$\frac{1}{12}$ of 24 = 2
$\frac{1}{24}$ of 24 = 1

$\frac{1}{2} + \frac{1}{3} = \frac{20}{24} = \frac{5}{6}$
$\frac{1}{3} + \frac{1}{4} = \frac{14}{24} = \frac{7}{12}$
$\frac{1}{2} + \frac{1}{6} = \frac{16}{24} = \frac{2}{3}$
$\frac{1}{4} + \frac{1}{6} = \frac{10}{24} = \frac{5}{12}$
$\frac{1}{4} + \frac{1}{12} = \frac{8}{24} = \frac{1}{3}$
$\frac{1}{6} + \frac{1}{24} = \frac{5}{24}$
etc.

Part 2 – development

PCM B:

The reason that Sharifa's solution works is that the three fractions, $\frac{1}{2}$, $\frac{1}{4}$ and $\frac{1}{8}$, do not add up to 1 (they add up to $\frac{7}{8}$), so they do not account for the whole group of camels.

Although it seems that each child ends up with the correct fraction of the camels, this is not quite true. Hamadi intended them to end up with fractions of 7:

Neema: $\frac{1}{2}$ of 7 = 3·5   Rashidi: $\frac{1}{4}$ of 7 = 1·75   Asim: $\frac{1}{8}$ of 7 = 0·875

What they end up with are fractions of 8:

Neema: $\frac{1}{2}$ of 8 = 4   Rashidi: $\frac{1}{4}$ of 8 = 2   Asim: $\frac{1}{8}$ of 8 = 1

Everyone will be happy with the solution because each child actually gets slightly more camels than the fractions of 7 would have resulted in, and no camels have to be cut into parts!

Investigations

$\frac{2}{3} = \frac{1}{2} + \frac{1}{6}$

$\frac{2}{5} = \frac{1}{3} + \frac{1}{15}$

$\frac{2}{7} = \frac{1}{4} + \frac{1}{28}$

$\frac{2}{9} = \frac{1}{5} + \frac{1}{45}$

Number of counters: 3 × 2 = 6
Target number: $\frac{2}{3}$ of 6 = 4
Largest unit fraction: $\frac{1}{2}$ of 6 = 3
Second unit fraction: $\frac{1}{6}$ of 6 = 1

Number of counters: 5 × 3 = 15
Target number: $\frac{2}{5}$ of 15 = 6
Largest unit fraction: $\frac{1}{3}$ of 15 = 5
Second unit fraction: $\frac{1}{15}$ of 15 = 1

Number of counters: 7 × 4 = 28
Target number: $\frac{2}{7}$ of 28 = 8
Largest unit fraction: $\frac{1}{4}$ of 28 = 7
Second unit fraction: $\frac{1}{28}$ of 28 = 1

Number of counters: 9 × 5 = 45
Target number: $\frac{2}{9}$ of 45 = 10
Largest unit fraction: $\frac{1}{5}$ of 45 = 9
Second unit fraction: $\frac{1}{45}$ of 45 = 1

Children may discover rules like this:

- Largest unit fraction = (target denominator ÷ 2) + 0·5.
- Number of counters = (target denominator) × (denominator of largest unit fraction)
- Second unit fraction = 1/number of counters

They should then be able to work out the pair of unit fractions for any fraction with a numerator of 2 (with the use of a calculator if necessary). For example:

$\frac{2}{11} = \frac{1}{6} + \frac{1}{66}$
$\frac{2}{19} = \frac{1}{10} + \frac{1}{190}$

$\frac{2}{13} = \frac{1}{7} + \frac{1}{91}$
$\frac{2}{25} = \frac{1}{13} + \frac{1}{325}$

$\frac{2}{15} = \frac{1}{8} + \frac{1}{120}$
$\frac{2}{51} = \frac{1}{26} + \frac{1}{1326}$

Year 4 Spring Assessment Activity

Number walls

Assessment Foci: L4 Using and applying mathematics (Problem solving; Communicating; Reasoning); L4 Number (numbers and the number system)
Resources: PCMs E–I; scissors; glue

Lesson 1 – preparation – 1 hour

Part 1 – introduction – 15 minutes
Copy this number wall onto the board.

Number walls are formed by adding the numbers in two adjacent cells and putting the result in the cell above. What is the top number in this wall?

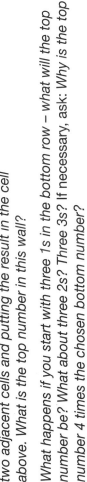

What happens if you start with three 1s in the bottom row – what will the top number be? What about three 2s? Three 3s? If necessary, ask: Why is the top number 4 times the chosen bottom number?

Part 2 – development – 30 minutes
Give children PCMs F and G. They investigate how three consecutive numbers in the bottom row of the wall must be arranged in order to give the largest or smallest top number. If necessary, ask: *Where is the smallest number in the bottom row? Where is the largest? What do you notice? Can you predict what the top number will be just by looking at the bottom row?*

Give children PCM H and another copy of PCM G. They make as many walls as they can with the top number 10, and then as many as they can with a top number of their own choice. They may start by using trial and error before identifying patterns and developing strategies. If necessary, remind them of their findings from PCM F (the middle number in the bottom row is added twice). *Add the numbers in the outside cells. Is the total odd or even? What do you notice?*

Extension: challenge children to work with number walls with four rows.

Part 3 – plenary – 15 minutes
Bring the group together for a discussion. Ask children to explain how they decided which numbers to put in the bottom rows of their walls, and what they discovered.

Lesson 2 – investigation – 1 hour

Part 1 – introduction – 15 minutes
Ask children to remind you of what they have discovered about number walls so far. Discuss ways of making three-row walls with the top number 12.

Give each child a copy of PCM I. They write brief initial ideas and conjectures about the investigation. Encourage them to plan how they will record their work.

Part 2 – investigation – 35 minutes
Children work individually to develop their lines of investigation, recording their journey and any findings.

They make hedra walls, which are pyramids with a flat top, that represent a three-row number wall on each face. Children are challenged to complete each face in a different way so that each face ends up with the number 12 in the top triangle. They should aim to make the six outer numbers (at the corners) different.

Encourage children to search for possibilities without using trial and error. Remind them of what they discovered in the preparation lesson, and encourage them to apply that knowledge to this investigation.

Extension: challenge children to make hedra walls with different top numbers. Encourage any creative open-ended further explorations.

Part 3 – conclusions – 10 minutes
Children write a final report of their investigation, showing their journey and findings along the way, with any conclusions or fresh ideas.

Ask children to complete the self-assessment sheet on PCM E.

Number walls

Objectives

These are the objectives that could be met by children doing this Assessment Activity.

Strand	Abacus Evolve objectives	Framework objectives
Using and applying mathematics	**Y4** Recognise and explain patterns and relationships, generalise and predict **Y4** Recognise the properties of odd and even numbers, including their sums and differences **Y4** Make and investigate a general statement about familiar numbers or shapes by finding examples that satisfy it (number)	**Y4** Represent a puzzle or problem using number sentences, statements or diagrams; use these to solve the problem; present and interpret the solution in the context of the problem **Y4** Suggest a line of enquiry and the strategy needed to follow it; collect, organise and interpret selected information to find answers **Y4** Identify and use patterns, relationships and properties of numbers or shapes; investigate a statement involving numbers and test it with examples **Y4** Report solutions to puzzles and problems, giving explanations and reasoning orally and in writing, using diagrams and symbols
Knowing and using number facts	**Y4** Add several 1-digit numbers **Y4** Consolidate understanding of the relationship between addition and subtraction **Y4** Find a small difference by counting on, e.g. 5003 − 4996	**Y4** Use knowledge of addition and subtraction facts and place value to derive sums and differences of pairs of multiples of 10, 100 or 1000

Answers

Note: these answers are not exhaustive.

Preparation

Part 1 – introduction

Children should notice that the centre number in the bottom row is added twice. If the three numbers in the bottom row are the same, the top number will be 4 times the chosen number.

		$a + 2b + c$		
	$a + b$		$b + c$	
a		b		c

		$(5 + 5 + 5 + 5)$		
	$5 + 5$		$5 + 5$	
5		5		5

Part 2 – development

PCM F: Given any three numbers in the bottom row, the smallest top number is made by placing the smallest of the three numbers in the bottom centre cell; the largest top number is made by placing the largest number in the bottom centre cell. Children may notice that the top numbers increase in 4s, and that, when the bottom numbers are arranged consecutively, the top number is 4 times the middle number.

Bottom number:	1, 2, 3	2, 3, 4	3, 4, 5	4, 5, 6
Smallest top number:	7	11	15	19
Top number when bottom numbers arranged consecutively:	8	12	16	20
Largest top number:	9	13	17	21

PCM H: Children should notice that if the sum of the outer numbers is even then the top number will be even; if the sum is odd, the top number will be odd. This is because twice the centre number will always be even, and odd + even = odd and even + even = even.

Bottom centre number = $\frac{1}{2}$ (target top number – sum of outer numbers)

Extension: in a four-row number wall, the top number is the sum of the outer cells in the bottom row plus 3 times the sum of inner cells in the bottom row.

Investigation

Children should by now have a thorough understanding of how number walls work and can concentrate on finding patterns.

Two possible solutions are:

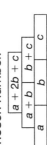

	12	
3		9
1	2	7

	12	
4		8
2	2	6

	12	
5		7
3	2	5

	12	
3		9
1	2	7

	12	
5		7
4	1	6

	12	
5		7
3	2	5

Year 4 Summer Assessment Activity   Tessellation

Assessment Foci: L4 Using and applying mathematics (Problem solving; Communicating; Reasoning); L4 Shape, space and measures (Properties of shape; Properties of position and movement)

Resources: PCMs E and J–K; thin card; scissors; square dot paper; example of tessellations (e.g. wallpaper); coloured pencils

Lesson 1 – preparation – 1 hour

Part 1 – introduction – 10 minutes

Give children the quadrilateral and triangle from PCM J, preferably photocopied onto thin card. Do not at this stage reveal that the shapes are two parts of a square. Ask children to discuss the shapes and their properties before investigating the shapes that can be made using the two pieces.

How many shapes can you make using this triangle and quadrilateral? Show children an example and explain that they should join sides of equal length to make their shapes.

Part 2 – development – 30 minutes

Now ask pairs to investigate how many shapes they can make using the triangle and quadrilateral. They record the shapes they make on square dot paper, adding descriptive notes about their properties.

Ask any children who seem satisfied they have found all the possible shapes: *Are you sure you have found them all? How do you know?* There are eight shapes to be found.

Extension: ask children to work together to add to their list of properties for each of the eight shapes, identifying any lines of symmetry, pairs of equal sides, pairs of parallel sides, pairs of equal angles and right angles.

Part 3 – plenary – 20 minutes

Hold a short discussion about what the group has found and recorded. Compare and check the different 2D shapes found. *Are any the same, but rotated or reflected? Why are there eight different shapes?*

Ask children to examine the two pieces and the eight shapes. *How many sides did you start with?* (3 + 4 = 7 sides) *How many sides do the combined shapes have?* (3, 4 or 5 sides) *Can you explain this?*

Explain to children that in the next lesson they are going to look at tessellations. Show them some examples (e.g. wrapping paper) and ask them to look for some more before the next lesson.

Lesson 2 – investigation – 1 hour

Part 1 – consolidation – 10 minutes

Give children the triangle and quadrilateral from PCM J. *Look at the angles in the original two shapes. Are any the same?* There are just four different sizes of angle in the original shapes, including right angles. *Colour each size of angle differently, using four colours – blue, green, red and yellow. How do these angles combine to make the angles of the eight shapes?*

Each of the eight shapes you made can be used to make infinite tile patterns without gaps. These are called tessellations. Demonstrate how the square tessellates.

Give children the triangle tessellation from the bottom of PCM J. *Colour the angles within the tessellation.*

Part 2 – investigation – 35 minutes

Give each child two copies of PCM K, preferably photocopied onto thin card. Explain the investigation: *These are six of the shapes you made from the triangle and quadrilateral. You are going to cut out the shapes and investigate tessellating them.*

Give children 5 minutes to write brief initial ideas and conjectures about the investigation. Encourage them to plan how they will record their work.

The shapes with more sides are likely to be trickier, so you may want to start with one of the quadrilaterals. Children should use one type of shape and build up a pattern until it becomes clear how the pattern could continue in all directions 'for ever'. Children can record the patterns by copying them onto square dot paper, or by sticking the pieces onto a plain sheet. They should explain why the tessellations work by colouring the angles.

Part 3 – conclusions – 15 minutes

Children write a final report of their investigation, showing their journey and findings along the way, with any conclusions or fresh ideas.

Ask children to complete the self-assessment sheet on PCM E.

Objectives

These are the objectives that could be met by children doing this Assessment Activity.

Strand	Abacus Evolve objectives	Framework objectives
Using and applying mathematics	**Y4** Recognise and explain patterns and relationships, generalise and predict **Y4** Make and investigate a general statement about familiar numbers or shapes by finding examples that satisfy it (shape)	**Y4** Represent a puzzle or problem using number sentences, statements or diagrams; use these to solve the problem; present and interpret the solution in the context of the problem **Y4** Suggest a line of enquiry and the strategy needed to follow it; collect, organise and interpret selected information to find answers **Y4** Identify and use patterns, relationships and properties of numbers or shapes; investigate a statement involving numbers and test it with examples **Y4** Report solutions to puzzles and problems, giving explanations and reasoning orally and in writing, using diagrams and symbols
Understanding shape	**Y4** Describe and visualise 2D shapes **Y4** Classify polygons using criteria such as number of right angles, and whether or not they are regular **Y4** Classify polygons according to their lines of symmetry	**Y4** Draw polygons and classify them by identifying their properties, including their line symmetry

Tessellation

Answers

Note: these answers are not exhaustive.

Preparation

Part 2 – development

Triangle: right-angled scalene

Quadrilateral: trapezium; one pair of parallel sides; one pair of equal sides; two pairs of equal angles; one line of reflection symmetry

Quadrilateral: parallelogram; two pairs of parallel sides; two pairs of equal sides; two pairs of equal angles; rotational symmetry order 2

Pentagon: three right angles; the other two angles are equal; three equal sides; the other two sides are equal

Quadrilateral: two right angles

Pentagon: one right angle; three equal sides; the other two sides are equal

Quadrilateral: square; four equal sides; four right angles; two pairs of parallel sides; four lines of reflection symmetry; rotational symmetry order 4

Pentagon: one right angle; two pairs of equal sides

Part 3 – plenary

Each side of the quadrilateral can be joined to one side of the triangle in two ways ($4 \times 2 = 8$ shapes). When two sides join, they are 'lost'. Maximum number of sides is $7 - 2 = 5$. Pairs of sides can link to make single sides.

Investigations

Part 1 – consolidation

The original two shapes have:
- three right angles (A)
- an obtuse angle (B)
- two large acute angles (C)
- a small acute angle (D).

C and D add to make a right angle, A.

D and A add to make B.

Combinations of these angles make straight lines and complete turns, so leaving no space between the shapes.

Part 2 – investigation

These are some of the possible tessellations:

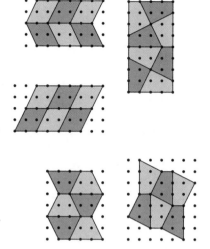

PCM Contents

Splitting one hundred

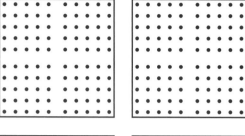
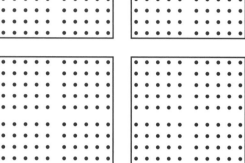

1 Draw one vertical line to split the dots into two groups. Write it as a multiplication in the grid. Repeat four times.

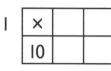

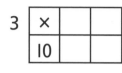
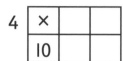

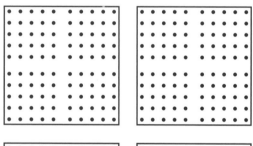

2 Draw one horizontal line to split the dots into two groups. Write it as a multiplication in the grid. Repeat four times.

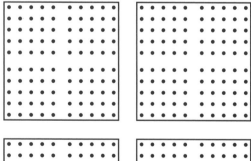
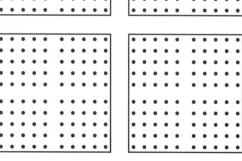

3 Now draw one vertical line and one horizontal line to split the dots into four groups. Write it as a multiplication in the grid. Repeat four times.

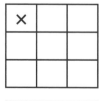
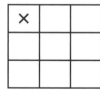

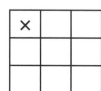

116

Abacus Evolve Year 4 Challenge PCM © Pearson Education Ltd 2009

Number pair game

A **245** How many more from 5874 to 6000?	**B** **245** How many more from 3895 to 4000?	**C** **245** How many more from 7185 to 8000?	**D** **245** How many more from 5978 to 6500?
A **126** How many more from 7837 to 8000?	**B** **105** How many more from 7200 to 9000?	**C** **815** How many more from 4374 to 4500?	**D** **522** How many more from 8685 to 9500?
A **163** How many more from 1478 to 2000?	**B** **1800** How many more from 5478 to 6000?	**C** **126** How many more from 6601 to 7000?	**D** **815** How many more from 1570 to 2000?
A **522** How many more from 6895 to 7000?	**B** **522** How many more from 7950 to 10 000?	**C** **399** How many more from 5700 to 7500?	**D** **430** How many more from 2950 to 5000?
A **105** How many more from 3570 to 4000?	**B** **2050** How many more from 4185 to 5000?	**C** **1800** How many more from 1450 to 3500?	**D** **2050** How many more from 5837 to 6000?
A **430** How many more from 9755 to 10 000?	**B** **815** How many more from 4255 to 4500?	**C** **2050** How many more from 4755 to 5000?	**D** **163** How many more from 7255 to 7500?

Abacus Evolve Year 4 Challenge PCM © Pearson Education Ltd 2009

Investigating 2D shapes

Abacus Evolve Year 4 Challenge PCM © Pearson Education Ltd 2009

Rotational symmetry

Draw another line to find the centre of rotational symmetry of this shape.

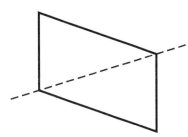

Investigate if these shapes have rotational symmetry.

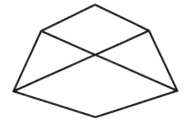
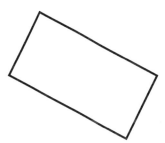

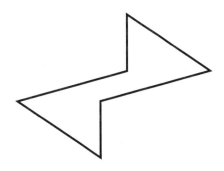

Abacus Evolve Year 4 Challenge PCM © Pearson Education Ltd 2009

2D shape patterns

right angle   acute   equilateral   line of symmetry
isosceles   obtuse   equal   scalene

Orange triangle	Green triangle	Purple triangle
I have three different length sides. I have three different sized angles. I have a **right** angle.	I have three different length sides. I have three different sized angles. I have an _____ angle.	I have three different length sides. I have three different sized angles. I have an _____ angle.
My name is **right** angled scalene triangle.	My name is _____ angled scalene triangle.	My name is _____ angled scalene triangle.

Red triangle	Yellow triangle
I have **just one line of symmetry**. I have a **right angle**.	I have _____ I have _____
So my name is **right angled isosceles triangle**.	So my name is _____

Blue triangle	White triangle
I have _____ I have _____	I have _____ All my angles _____ All my sides _____
So my name is _____	So my name is _____

Abacus Evolve Year 4 Challenge PCM © Pearson Education Ltd 2009

Areas of rectangles

Abacus Evolve Year 4 Challenge PCM © Pearson Education Ltd 2009

Showing data in different ways

A family has two cars. Here is the carbon cost data, in kilograms, of 12 journeys made in each of the cars.

Carbon cost of 12 journeys in the small car (kg)											
32	12	18	24	8	36	10	20	24	32	12	36

Carbon cost of 12 journeys in the large car (kg)											
48	18	27	36	12	54	15	30	36	48	18	54

1 Make two frequency tables, one for each type of car. Decide the best way to group the data.

This is an example of a pictogram. It shows the number of hours, to the nearest hour, that children spend watching television at the weekend.

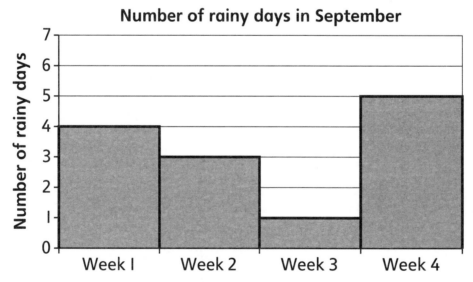

2 Draw a pictogram using the small car frequency table.
3 Draw a pictogram using the large car frequency table.

This is an example of a bar graph. It shows the number of rainy days in September.

Number of rainy days in September

4 Draw a bar graph using the small car frequency table.
5 Draw a bar graph using the large car frequency table.
6 Compare your graphs and discuss how they represent the data.

Abacus Evolve Year 4 Challenge PCM © Pearson Education Ltd 2009

All sorts of bears

Giant pandas live in China. They have large black patches around their eyes.	**Sun bears** (honey bears) live in Southeast Asia. They are a vulnerable species.
Spectacled bears live in South America. They have black fur with a pale marking on their face like spectacles.	**Sloth bears** live in or near India. They mainly eat insects.
Polar bears live in the Arctic Circle, near the North Pole. They mainly eat seals.	**Asiatic black bears** live in Asia. They are a vulnerable species.
American black bears live in North and Central America. They hibernate in the winter.	**Brown bears** mostly eat plants and fish, but also small mammals. They are not a vulnerable species.

Abacus Evolve Year 4 Challenge PCM © Pearson Education Ltd 2009

Hexadria

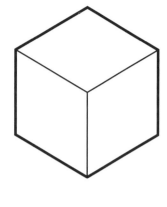 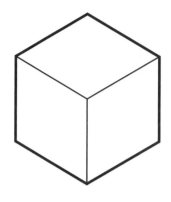

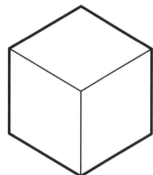 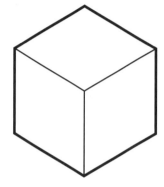 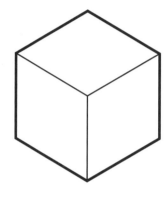

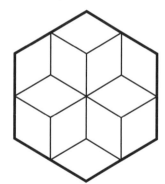 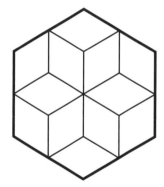 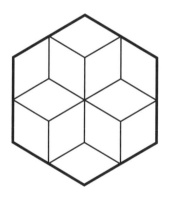

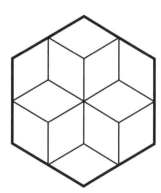 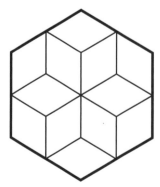 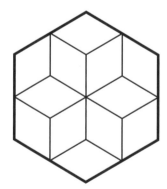

Abacus Evolve Year 4 Challenge PCM © Pearson Education Ltd 2009

Adding and subtracting near decades

Decade numbers are 10, 20, 30, 40, 50, 60, and so on.

Complete these additions and subtractions mentally.

1 $40 + 30 = \boxed{}$

2 $50 + \boxed{} = 90$

3 $80 - 30 = \boxed{}$

4 $100 - \boxed{} = 40$

5 $\boxed{} - 20 = 80 - \boxed{}$

6 $100 - \boxed{} = \boxed{} + 20$

Near decade numbers are just 1 or 2 away from decade numbers.
You can calculate using the nearest decade number, then adjust.

Find the answers to these missing number questions.

7 $40 + 29 = \boxed{}$

8 $70 - \boxed{} = 31$

Now try to work these out in your head.
When there are two boxes, both numbers are the same.

9 $42 + 39 = \boxed{}$

10 $88 - \boxed{} = 29$

11 $79 + 19 = \boxed{}$

12 $\boxed{} - 59 = 38$

13 $\boxed{} - 22 = 78$

14 $79 - \boxed{} = 41 + \boxed{}$

15 $\boxed{} + 11 = 89 - \boxed{}$

16 $62 - \boxed{} = \boxed{} + 18$

Abacus Evolve Year 4 Challenge PCM © Pearson Education Ltd 2009

Before and after the hour

A **9:45** 30 minutes later	**B** **9:45** 20 minutes later	**C** **9:45** 25 minutes later	**D** **9:45** 40 minutes later
A **10:15** 35 minutes earlier	**B** **10:05** 30 minutes earlier	**C** **10:10** 15 minutes earlier	**D** **10:25** 55 minutes earlier
A **9:40** 25 minutes later	**B** **9:35** 50 minutes later	**C** **9:55** 20 minutes later	**D** **9:30** 50 minutes later
A **10:05** 35 minutes earlier	**B** **10:25** 30 minutes earlier	**C** **10:15** 40 minutes earlier	**D** **10:20** 40 minutes earlier
A **9:30** 40 minutes later	**B** **9:55** 25 minutes later	**C** **9:35** 30 minutes later	**D** **9:40** 35 minutes later
A **10:10** 25 minutes earlier	**B** **10:20** 35 minutes earlier	**C** **10:05** 20 minutes earlier	**D** **10:15** 30 minutes earlier

Abacus Evolve Year 4 Challenge PCM © Pearson Education Ltd 2009

Time zones

Plot this journey on the world time zones map on PCM I3.

Stage	From	To	Time difference	Change
I	London, England	Berlin, Germany	I hour	Later
2	Berlin, Germany	Singapore	7 hours	Later
3	Singapore	Melbourne, Australia	2 hours	Later
4	Melbourne, Australia	Los Angeles, USA	6 hours	Later
5	Los Angeles, USA	New York, USA	3 hours	Later
6	New York, USA	London, England	5 hours	Later

Imagine a six-step journey of your own around the world travelling west.

Complete this table.

Stage	From	To	Time difference	Change
I	London		hours	Earlier
2			hours	Earlier
3			hours	Earlier
4			hours	Earlier
5			hours	Earlier
6		London	hours	Earlier

Abacus Evolve Year 4 Challenge PCM © Pearson Education Ltd 2009

World time zones map

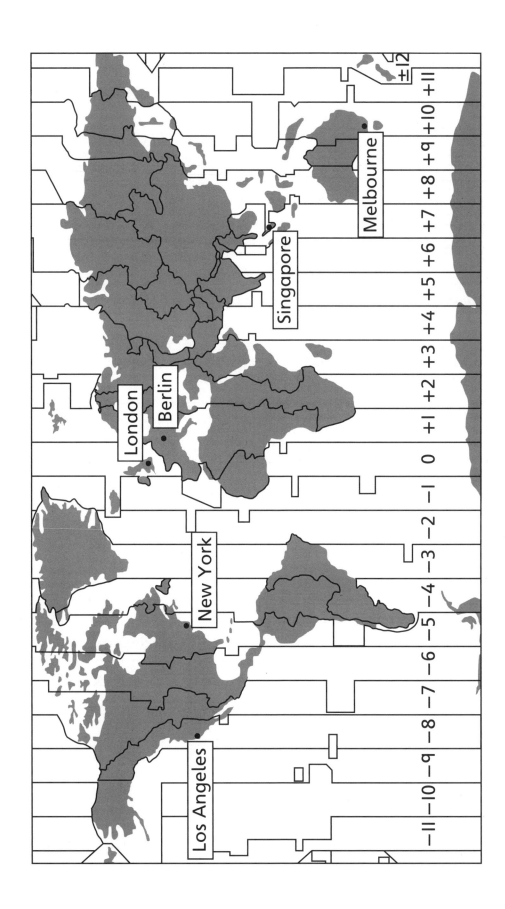

Abacus Evolve Year 4 Challenge PCM © Pearson Education Ltd 2009

Sum, difference and product

MPC

The two numbers are

_____ and _____

Their sum is _____

Their difference is ____

Their product is _____

MPC

The two numbers are

_____ and _____

Their sum is _____

Their difference is ____

Their product is _____

MPC

The two numbers are

_____ and _____

Their sum is _____

Their difference is ____

Their product is _____

MPC

The two numbers are

_____ and _____

Their sum is _____

Their difference is ____

Their product is _____

MPC

The two numbers are

_____ and _____

Their sum is _____

Their difference is ____

Their product is _____

MPC

The two numbers are

_____ and _____

Their sum is _____

Their difference is ____

Their product is _____

MPC

The two numbers are

_____ and _____

Their sum is _____

Their difference is ____

Their product is _____

MPC

The two numbers are

_____ and _____

Their sum is _____

Their difference is ____

Their product is _____

MPC

The two numbers are

_____ and _____

Their sum is _____

Their difference is ____

Their product is _____

Rainbow patterns

1	2	3	4	5	6	7	8	9	10	11	12	13	14	15	16	17	18	19	20
20	40	60	80	100	120	140	160	180	200										
19	38	57	76	95	114	133	152	171	190										
18	36	54	72	90	108	126	144	162	180										
17	34	51	68	85	102	119	136	153	170										
16	32	48	64	80	96	112	128	144	160										
15	30	45	60	75	90	105	120	135	150										
14	28	42	56	70	84	98	112	126	140										
13	26	39	52	65	78	91	104	117	130	143									
12	24	36	48	60	72	84	96	108	120	132	144								
11	22	33	44	55	66	77	88	99	110	121	132	143							
10	20	30	40	50	60	70	80	90	100	110	120	130	140	150	160	170	180	190	200
9	18	27	36	45	54	63	72	81	90	99	108	117	126	135	144	153	162	171	180
8	16	24	32	40	48	56	64	72	80	88	96	104	112	120	128	136	144	152	160
7	14	21	28	35	42	49	56	63	70	77	84	91	98	105	112	119	126	133	140
6	12	18	24	30	36	42	48	54	60	66	72	78	84	90	96	102	108	114	120
5	10	15	20	25	30	35	40	45	50	55	60	65	70	75	80	85	90	95	100
4	8	12	16	20	24	28	32	36	40	44	48	52	56	60	64	68	72	76	80
3	6	9	12	15	18	21	24	27	30	33	36	39	42	45	48	51	54	57	60
2	4	6	8	10	12	14	16	18	20	22	24	26	28	30	32	34	36	38	40
1	2	3	4	5	6	7	8	9	10	11	12	13	14	15	16	17	18	19	20

Abacus Evolve Year 4 Challenge PCM © Pearson Education Ltd 2009

Investigating fraction sentences

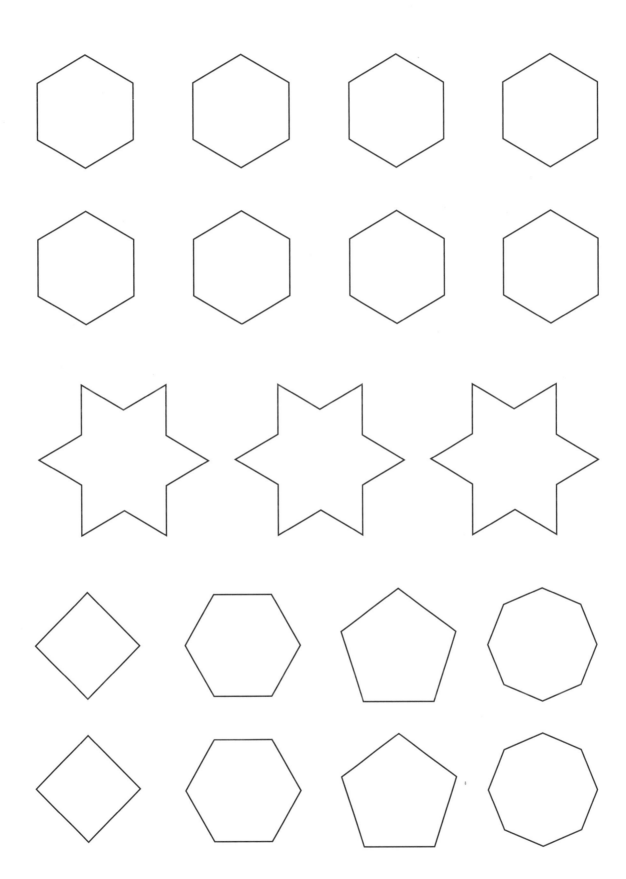

Abacus Evolve Year 4 Challenge PCM © Pearson Education Ltd 2009

Estimating game

Calculation:	Estimates			
Name(s)	Between	Difference	In/Out	Rank

The answer is:

✂ -

Calculation:	Estimates			
Name(s)	Between	Difference	In/Out	Rank

The answer is:

✂ -

Calculation:	Estimates			
Name(s)	Between	Difference	In/Out	Rank

The answer is:

✂ -

Calculation:	Estimates			
Name(s)	Between	Difference	In/Out	Rank

The answer is:

Abacus Evolve Year 4 Challenge PCM © Pearson Education Ltd 2009

Six circles

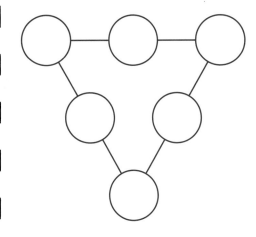

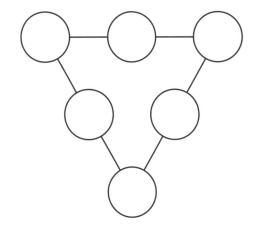

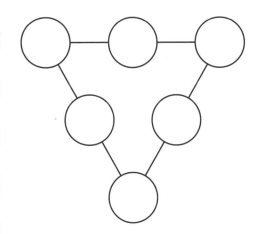

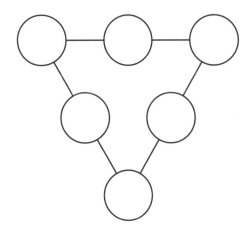

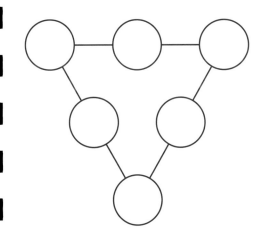

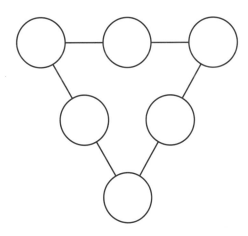

Abacus Evolve Year 4 Challenge PCM © Pearson Education Ltd 2009

Exploring arithmagons

1

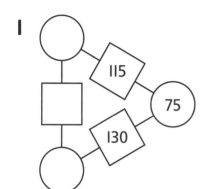

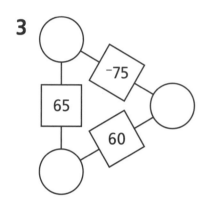

2

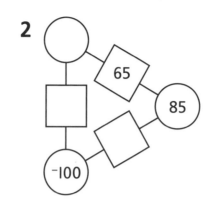

3

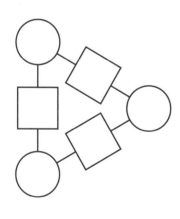

4

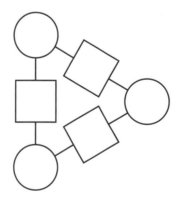

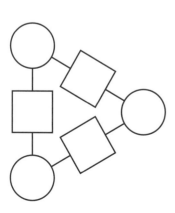

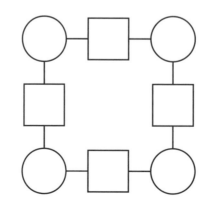

Abacus Evolve Year 4 Challenge PCM © Pearson Education Ltd 2009

Positive and negative number loops

Abacus Evolve Year 4 Challenge PCM © Pearson Education Ltd 2009

A	B	C	D
0 Subtract 25	**0** Add 14	**0** Subtract 28	**0** Add 64
$^-$25 Add 40	**$^+$14** Subtract 34	**$^-$28** Add 60	**$^+$64** Subtract 76
$^+$15 Add 35	**$^-$20** Add 70	**$^+$32** Subtract 18	**$^-$12** Add 26
$^+$50 Subtract 70	**$^+$50** Subtract 35	**$^+$14** Subtract 26	**$^+$14** Add 18
$^-$20 Add 34	**$^+$15** Subtract 40	**$^-$12** Add 76	**$^+$32** Subtract 60
$^+$14 Subtract 14	**$^-$25** Add 25	**$^+$64** Subtract 64	**$^-$28** Add 28

Halving and doubling shapes

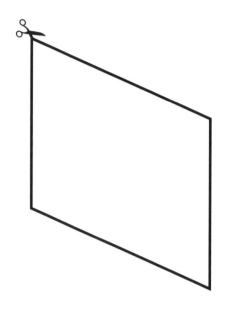

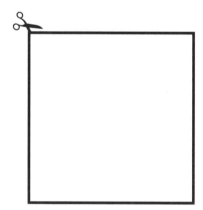

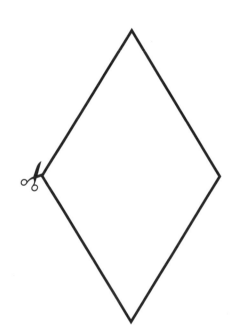

Abacus Evolve Year 4 Challenge PCM © Pearson Education Ltd 2009

Understanding tetrahedra

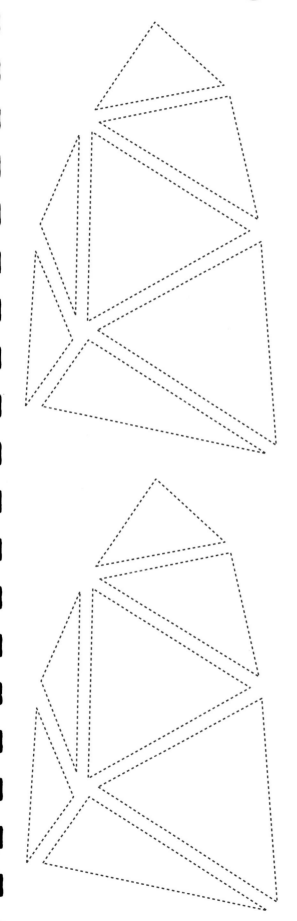

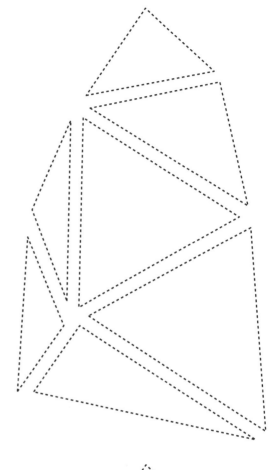

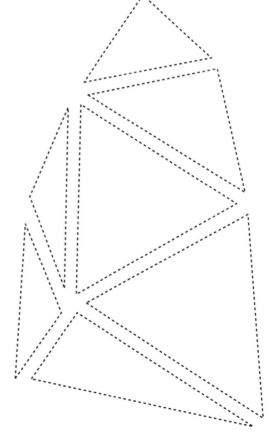

Abacus Evolve Year 4 Challenge PCM © Pearson Education Ltd 2009

Properties of polyhedra I

Prisms

	Number of vertices	Number of edges	Number of faces
Triangular prism	6		5
Square prism			
Pentagonal prism			
Hexagonal prism			
Decagonal prism			

Pyramids

	Number of vertices	Number of edges	Number of faces
Triangular pyramid	4	6	4
Square pyramid	5		5
Pentagonal pyramid			
Hexagonal pyramid			
Decagonal pyramid			

Abacus Evolve Year 4 Challenge PCM © Pearson Education Ltd 2009

Properties of polyhedra 2

	Number of triangles	Number of rectangles	Number of pentagons	Number of hexagons	Number of decagons
Triangular prism					
Square prism					
Pentagonal prism					
Hexagonal prism					
Decagonal prism					
Triangular pyramid					
Square pyramid					
Pentagonal pyramid					
Hexagonal pyramid					
Decagonal pyramid					

Abacus Evolve Year 4 Challenge PCM © Pearson Education Ltd 2009

Nomograms

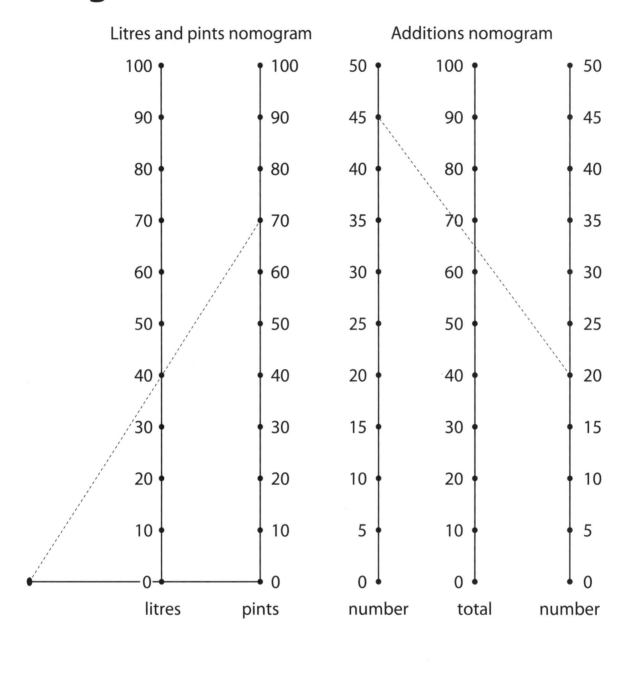

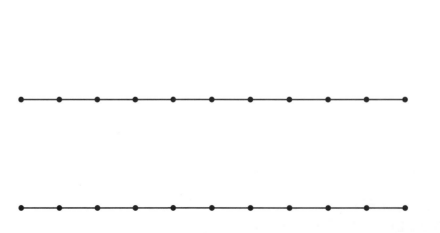

Blank nomogram

Timetables

Trains between London and Arundel

Station	Train 1	Train 2	Train 3	Train 4	Train 5
London Victoria	06:02	06:32	06:47	07:17	08:07
Change trains at Three Bridges			arr: 07:24 dep: 07:30		arr: 08:41 dep: 08:45
Arundel	07:39	08:14	08:14	08:50	09:31

Flying with *FlyTee*

This is the timetable of routes and flight times for *FlyTee*.
All flight times are in minutes.

Airport To From	Bel	Bir	Car	Edi	Man	New	Sou	Sta
Belfast		55	50	40	35			
Birmingham	55			45			55	40
Cardiff	50			70	40	65		
Edinburgh	40	45	70				90	60
Manchester	35		40			30	65	55
Newcastle			65		30		80	50
Southampton		55		90	65	80		
Stansted		40		60	55	50		

FlyTee flights:
- Early morning flights leave at 07:00.
- Mid-morning flights leave at 10:30.
- Early evening flights leave at 19:00.

Check-in and departure information:
- Passengers should always arrive at the airport 40 minutes before their flight departs.
- At the end of a flight, it can take up to 30 minutes to collect baggage and leave the airport.

Abacus Evolve Year 4 Challenge PCM © Pearson Education Ltd 2009

Perimeter and area

Rectangles

Perimeter	Area	Side 1	Side 2
26 cm	42 cm²		
28 cm	49 cm²		
30 cm	44 cm²		
24 cm	20 cm²		
20 cm	24 cm²		
24 cm	36 cm²		
26 cm	36 cm²		
42 cm	90 cm²		

Symmetrical hexagons

Perimeter	Short side length	Long side length
15 cm		3 cm
21 cm	1 cm	
24 cm		6 cm
27 cm	4 cm	

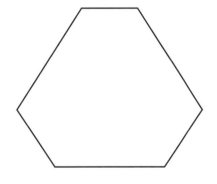

Kites and rhombuses

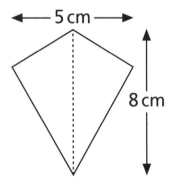

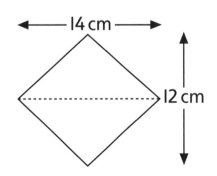

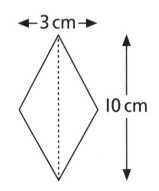

Area_____

Area_____

Area_____

Abacus Evolve Year 4 Challenge PCM © Pearson Education Ltd 2009

Abacus Evolve Year 4 Challenge PCM © Pearson Education Ltd 2009

Graphs and collecting data

Data collection sheet	
Collected by: Jin	
Walking	1, 2, 5, 3, 1, 2, 5, 2, 3, 4
Bicycle	4, 3, 1, 0, 5, 3, 1, 4, 2, 2
Bus	0, 1, 0, 2, 3, 3, 1, 0, 0, 2
Train	0, 0, 0, 2, 0, 0, 0, 0, 0, 2
Car	2, 0, 2, 1, 1, 2, 1, 2, 1, 0

Data collection sheet	
Collected by: Ravi	
Walking	0, 2, 1, 2, 1, 1, 0, 3, 3, 0
Bicycle	0, 0, 0, 0, 0, 0, 0, 0, 0, 0
Bus	0, 2, 2, 0, 0, 2, 0, 2, 0, 0
Train	0, 2, 0, 0, 0, 2, 0, 0, 0, 0
Car	6, 4, 4, 6, 6, 4, 2, 3, 2, 4

Data collection sheet	
Collected by: Carys	
Walking	4, 6, 3, 2, 4, 5, 3, 4, 6, 3
Bicycle	0, 0, 2, 2, 2, 2, 2, 0, 0, 2
Bus	0, 0, 0, 0, 0, 0, 0, 0, 0, 0
Train	2, 0, 0, 0, 0, 0, 0, 2, 0, 0
Car	2, 2, 0, 0, 2, 0, 2, 2, 2, 0

Data collection sheet	
Collected by: David	
Walking	3, 3, 4, 2, 3, 3, 4, 3, 2, 3
Bicycle	3, 4, 1, 1, 1, 1, 1, 4, 4, 1
Bus	0, 0, 0, 2, 0, 0, 2, 0, 0, 0
Train	0, 0, 2, 0, 2, 2, 0, 0, 0, 2
Car	1, 3, 4, 1, 2, 0, 0, 3, 2, 1

Palindromes

11	12	13	14	15	16	17	18	19
20	21	22	23	24	25	26	27	28
29	30	31	32	33	34	35	36	37
38	39	40	41	42	43	44	45	46
47	48	49	50	51	52	53	54	55
56	57	58	59	60	61	62	63	64
65	66	67	68	69	70	71	72	73
74	75	76	77	78	79	80	81	82
83	84	85	86	87	88	89	90	91
92	93	94	95	96	97	98	99	

Abacus Evolve Year 4 Challenge PCM © Pearson Education Ltd 2009

Subtraction matching game

Set 3 £4.81	Set 2 £1.51	Set 1 £6.32	
Set 3 £4.75	Set 2 £1.49	Set 1 £6.24	
Set 3 £4.82	Set 2 £1.66	Set 1 £6.48	
Set 3 £4.76	Set 2 £1.54	Set 1 £6.30	
Set 3 £4.93	Set 2 £1.52	Set 1 £6.45	
Set 3 £4.77	Set 2 £1.42	Set 1 £6.19	
Set 3 £4.84	Set 2 £1.59	Set 1 £6.43	
Set 3 £4.79	Set 2 £1.43	Set 1 £6.22	
Set 3 £4.88	Set 2 £1.61	Set 1 £6.49	

Abacus Evolve Year 4 Challenge PCM © Pearson Education Ltd 2009

The bill

The Sunburnt Prawn
Menu

Starters

Oysters with lemon and lime sauce	$30·50
Red pepper soup	$34·90
Pork and apple fritters	$36·50
Salmon with orange salad	$38·90
The Sunburnt Prawn taster plate	$48·50

Main courses

Chicken Kiev with tomato and sweet potato	$62·90
Roast lamb with potatoes and parsnips	$68·90
Pork loin and bean salsa with apple chutney	$66·90
Roasted kingfish with sweetcorn and rice	$64·90
Steak with mushrooms and mashed potato	$72·50
Goat's cheese with beetroot salad and vine tomato	$48·90

Desserts

Bread pudding with pineapple and mango	$28·50
Lemon surprise with apple and vanilla	$29·90
Dark chocolate mousse with banana	$32·90
Strawberry cheesecake with ice-cream	$30·90
The Sunburnt Prawn dessert taster plate	$46·90
Cheese board – a selection of three cheeses	$48·00

Drinks

Coffee:

Espresso, latte, cappuccino or American	$20·50

Tea:

Speciality	$22·50
Ceylon	$16·50
China	$18·90

Abacus Evolve Year 4 Challenge PCM © Pearson Education Ltd 2009

Abacus Evolve Year 4 Challenge PCM © Pearson Education Ltd 2009

High score squares I

- Write the digits 1–9 in any order in a 3 by 3 grid.
- Each row is a 3-digit number.
- Add up the three 3-digit numbers from the rows.
- Each column is a 3-digit number.
- Add up the three 3-digit numbers from the columns.
- Subtract the column total from the row total to get your score.

This square scores 270.

3	1	7	317
2	8	6	+286
9	4	5	+945
			=1548
329	+184	+765	=1278
			1548 − 1278 = **270**

1 Can you make a score higher than 270? Try it using one of the blank tables on PCM 33.

2 What is the highest score you can find?
Think carefully about where to put the numbers.

High score squares 2

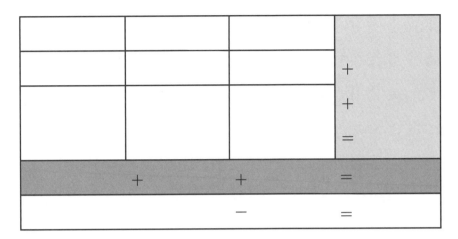

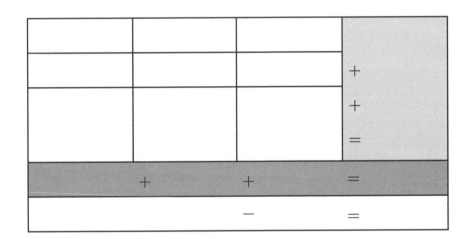

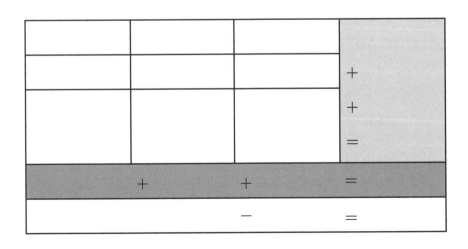

Abacus Evolve Year 4 Challenge PCM © Pearson Education Ltd 2009

Multiplying by doubling and halving

1

24 × 9	
24	9
	4
~~96~~	2
	1

2

35 × 12	
~~35~~	12
	6
140	
	1

3

23 × 14	
~~23~~	14
	3
184	1

4

27 × 13	
~~27~~	13
54	6
108	3
216	1
54 + 108 + 216 = 378	

5

21 × 19	
~~21~~	19
42	9
~~84~~	4
~~168~~	2
336	1
42 + 336 = 378	

6

29 × 16	
~~29~~	16
~~58~~	8
~~116~~	4
~~236~~	2
472	1
29 + 472 = 501	

Abacus Evolve Year 4 Challenge PCM © Pearson Education Ltd 2009

Into the unknown

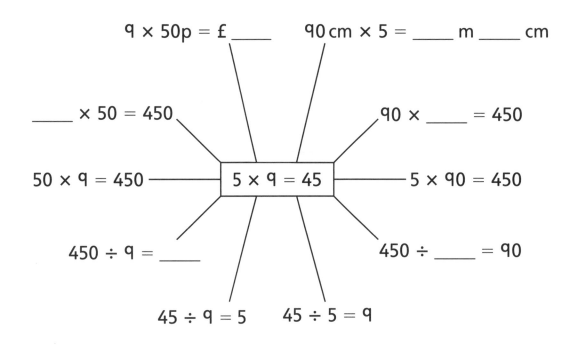

$9 \times 50p = £$ _____ $90\,cm \times 5 =$ _____ m _____ cm

_____ $\times 50 = 450$ $90 \times$ _____ $= 450$

$50 \times 9 = 450$ —— $5 \times 9 = 45$ —— $5 \times 90 = 450$

$450 \div 9 =$ _____ $450 \div$ _____ $= 90$

$45 \div 9 = 5$ $45 \div 5 = 9$

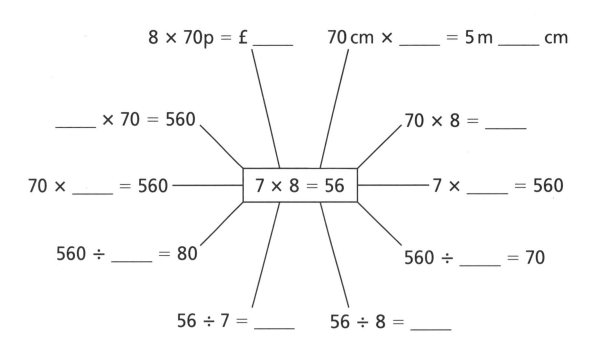

$8 \times 70p = £$ _____ $70\,cm \times$ _____ $= 5\,m$ _____ cm

_____ $\times 70 = 560$ $70 \times 8 =$ _____

$70 \times$ _____ $= 560$ —— $7 \times 8 = 56$ —— $7 \times$ _____ $= 560$

$560 \div$ _____ $= 80$ $560 \div$ _____ $= 70$

$56 \div 7 =$ _____ $56 \div 8 =$ _____

Abacus Evolve Year 4 Challenge PCM © Pearson Education Ltd 2009

Fractions in order I

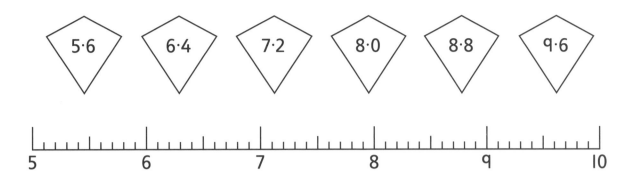

5·6   6·4   7·2   8·0   8·8   9·6

5   6   7   8   9   10

Kite cards

17 halves	76 tenths	59 tenths	5·1
$9\frac{1}{5}$	7·9	$6\frac{1}{5}$	53 tenths
95 tenths	81 tenths	6·8	11 halves

Ladder cards

15 fifths	3·2	36 tenths	39 tenths	$3\frac{1}{2}$
$3\frac{3}{4}$	3·3	3·7	31 tenths	7 halves
$3\frac{1}{4}$	34 tenths	3·8	20 fifths	3·5

Abacus Evolve Year 4 Challenge PCM © Pearson Education Ltd 2009

Fractions in order 2

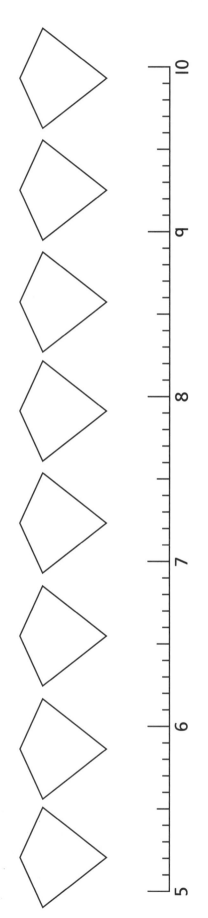

Abacus Evolve Year 4 Challenge PCM © Pearson Education Ltd 2009

Tenths link cards

A **2·4** How many tenths in 4·2?	**B** **2·4** What is half-way between 9 and 12?	**C** **2·4** How many fifths in 16·2?	**D** **2·4** How many fifths in 10·4?
A **42** What is 16 tenths?	**B** **10·5** How many tenths in 5·8?	**C** **81** How many halves in 21?	**D** **52** How many halves in 40·5?
A **1·6** How many tenths in 5·2?	**B** **58** How many halves in 26?	**C** **42** How many tenths in 3·9?	**D** **81** How many fifths in 7·2?
A **52** What is 105 tenths?	**B** **52** What is 29 tenths?	**C** **39** How many halves in 29?	**D** **36** What is half-way between 2·8 and 3?
A **10·5** How many tenths in 3·6?	**B** **2·9** How many tenths in 8·1?	**C** **58** What is half-way between 2·4 and 3·4?	**D** **2·9** What is half-way between 1·2 and 2?
A **36** What is 24 tenths?	**B** **81** What is half-way between 2 and 2·8?	**C** **2·9** What is half-way between 1·4 and 3·4?	**D** **1·6** What is half-way between 1·9 and 2·9?

Abacus Evolve Year 4 Challenge PCM © Pearson Education Ltd 2009

Rounding link cards 1: the nearest £10

A **£70** 4 × £5·90	B **£70** 5 × £6·99	C **£70** 6 × £9·25	D **£70** 3 × £14·99
A **£20** 6 × £5·90	B **£30** 6 × £9·15	C **£60** 3 × £8·30	D **£40** 6 × £5·80
A **£40** 4 × £11·30	B **£50** 5 × £11·05	C **£20** 5 × £10·99	D **£30** 5 × £3·10
A **£50** 3 × £21·65	B **£60** 4 × £8·99	C **£50** 3 × £8·45	D **£20** 3 × £15·05
A **£60** 4 × £6·30	B **£40** 6 × £4·15	C **£30** 5 × £8·90	D **£50** 4 × £13·90
A **£30** 5 × £13·10	B **£20** 3 × £24·99	C **£40** 6 × £10·90	D **£60** 4 × £18·50

Abacus Evolve Year 4 Challenge PCM © Pearson Education Ltd 2009

Rounding link cards 2: the nearest £5

A **£100** 3 × £38	**B** **£100** 4 × £22	**C** **£100** 5 × £20·60	**D** **£100** 6 × £18
A **£115** 3 × £36	**B** **£90** 4 × £24	**C** **£105** 5 × £23·20	**D** **£110** 6 × £15·25
A **£110** 3 × £31	**B** **£95** 4 × £26	**C** **£115** 5 × £18·60	**D** **£90** 6 × £19
A **£95** 3 × £35·50	**B** **£105** 4 × £28	**C** **£95** 5 × £18·25	**D** **£115** 6 × £16
A **£105** 3 × £29·50	**B** **£110** 4 × £29	**C** **£90** 5 × £21·60	**D** **£95** 6 × £17·20
A **£90** 3 × £33	**B** **£115** 4 × £24·50	**C** **£110** 5 × £20·40	**D** **£105** 6 × £17

Abacus Evolve Year 4 Challenge PCM © Pearson Education Ltd 2009

The Gattegno chart

	1	2	3	4	5	6	7	8	9
10 000 000									
1 000 000							7 000 000		
100 000		200 000							
10 000					50 000				
1000	1000	2000	3000	4000	5000	6000	7000	8000	9000
100	100	200	300	400	500	600	700	800	900
10	10	20	30	40	50	60	70	80	90
1	1	2	3	4	5	6	7	8	9
0·1								0·8	
0·01						0·06			
0·001			0·003						
0·0001									0·000 9
0·00001				0·000 04					

Abacus Evolve Year 4 Challenge PCM © Pearson Education Ltd 2009

Subtraction walls

Abacus Evolve Year 4 Challenge PCM © Pearson Education Ltd 2009

Matching subtractions

919 − 575	933 − 589	908 − 550	902 − 544	977 − 749
830 − 475	844 − 489	798 − 450	803 − 455	817 − 549
652 − 275	666 − 289	688 − 350	704 − 366	737 − 449
563 − 175	577 − 189	628 − 300	605 − 277	657 − 349
474 − 75	488 − 89	408 − 100	407 − 99	527 − 199
				905 − 677
				725 − 457
				635 − 347
				545 − 237
				455 − 127

Abacus Evolve Year 4 Challenge PCM © Pearson Education Ltd 2009

Multiplying and dividing by 9

Set A

2178	2349	2475	2574	2601
2673	2754	2817	2898	2925
121 × 18	29 × 81	55 × 45	143 × 18	289 × 9
33 × 81	153 × 18	313 × 9	46 × 63	65 × 45

Set B

414 ÷ 18	432 ÷ 24	468 ÷ 36	486 ÷ 18	522 ÷ 18
540 ÷ 45	558 ÷ 18	576 ÷ 36	612 ÷ 36	630 ÷ 30
23	18	13	27	29
12	31	16	17	21

Abacus Evolve Year 4 Challenge PCM © Pearson Education Ltd 2009

Digital roots

0	1	2	3	4	5	6	7	8
9	10	11	12	13	14	15	16	17
18	19	20	21	22	23	24	25	26
27	28	29	30	31	32	33	34	35
36	37	38	39	40	41	42	43	44
45	46	47	48	49	50	51	52	53
54	55	56	57	58	59	60	61	62
63	64	65	66	67	68	69	70	71
72	73	74	75	76	77	78	79	80
81	82	83	84	85	86	87	88	89
90	91	92	93	94	95	96	97	98

Abacus Evolve Year 4 Challenge PCM © Pearson Education Ltd 2009

Paper-folding angles

Use these instructions to make $\frac{1}{3}$ of a right angle, $\frac{2}{3}$ of a right angle, $1\frac{1}{3}$ of a right angle and $1\frac{2}{3}$ of a right angle.

Fold a piece of A4 paper in half length-ways.

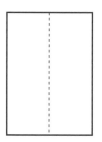

Fold the bottom left corner up to the middle, like this. This makes $\frac{2}{3}$ of a right angle in the bottom right corner.

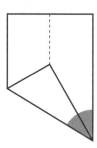

Fold the top right corner over, like this. This makes $\frac{1}{3}$ of a right angle in the bottom right corner.

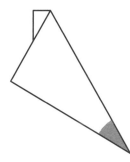

Make $\frac{1}{3}$ of a right angle then unfold your paper. In the creases you will see $1\frac{2}{3}$ of a right angle and $1\frac{1}{3}$ of a right angle.

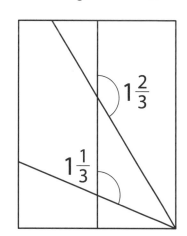

Abacus Evolve Year 4 Challenge PCM © Pearson Education Ltd 2009

Maps

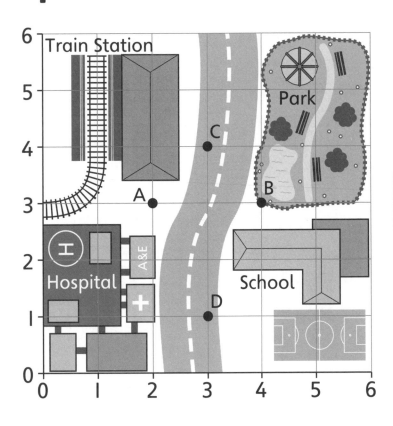

Abacus Evolve Year 4 Challenge PCM © Pearson Education Ltd 2009

1   What are the coordinates of point A? _____

2   What are the coordinates of point B? _____

3   How far is point A from point B on the map? _____

4   How far is point A from point B in real life? _____

5   What are the coordinates of point C? _____

6   What are the coordinates of point D? _____

7   How far is point C from point D on the map? _____

8   How far is point C from point D in real life? _____

9   Make up your own scale and coordinates questions using this
    map and your local maps. Swap questions with others in your
    group.

Half-price sale

Striped jumper

WAS: £78·00
NOW: £50·00

Pocket detail shirt

WAS: £64·00
NOW: £59·00

T-shirt
WAS: £13·00
NOW: £9·00

Socks
WAS: £14·00
NOW: £5·00

Ladies evening dress

WAS: £56·00
NOW: £25·00

Men's golf shorts

WAS: £39·00
NOW: £23·00

Men's suit

WAS: £150·00
NOW: £75·00

Jeans

WAS: £64·00
NOW: £57·00

Denim shorts

WAS: £23·00
NOW: £12·00

Sun hat
WAS: £22·00
NOW: £15·00

Women's golf shorts

WAS: £36·00
NOW: £22·00

Plain white polo shirt

WAS: £31·00
NOW: £20·00

Black polo shirt

WAS: £34·00
NOW: £31·00

Baseball cap

WAS: £24·00
NOW: £17·00

High heels
WAS: £67·00
NOW: £44·67

Polo neck jumper

WAS: £100·00
NOW: £90·00

Plain white shirt

WAS: £34·00
NOW: £14·00

Men's blazer

WAS: £70·00
NOW: £48·00

Which items are:

1 a little more than 50% off?
2 exactly half price?
3 a little less than 50% off?
4 a little more than $\frac{1}{3}$ off?
5 exactly $\frac{1}{3}$ off?
6 a little less than $\frac{1}{3}$ off?
7 about $\frac{1}{10}$ off?

Abacus Evolve Year 4 Challenge PCM © Pearson Education Ltd 2009

A nomogram

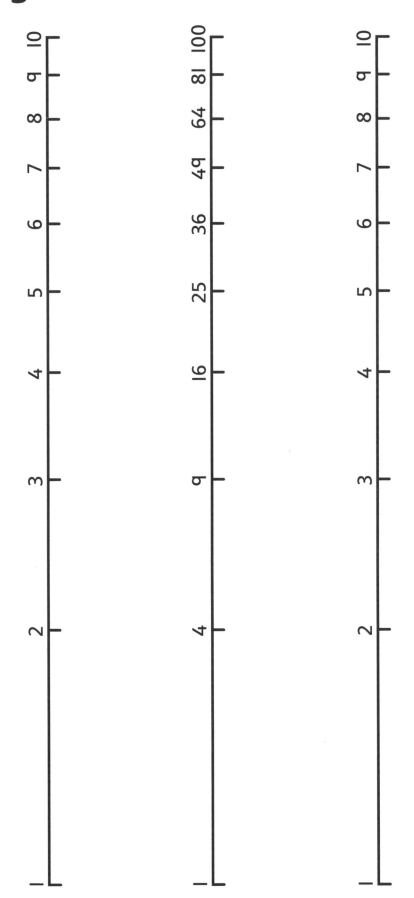

Abacus Evolve Year 4 Challenge PCM © Pearson Education Ltd 2009

Multiplying odd and even numbers

Number cards set A

3	5	7	9
12	14	16	18

Number cards set B

11	12	13	14
15	16	17	18
19	20	21	22
23	24	25	26
27	28	29	30
31	32		

Abacus Evolve Year 4 Challenge PCM © Pearson Education Ltd 2009

Factor record-breakers

1	2	3	4	5	6	7	8	9	10	11	12
13	14	15	16	17	18	19	20	21	22	23	24
25	26	27	28	29	30	31	32	33	34	35	36
37	38	39	40	41	42	43	44	45	46	47	48
49	50	51	52	53	54	55	56	57	58	59	60
61	62	63	64	65	66	67	68	69	70	71	72
73	74	75	76	77	78	79	80	81	82	83	84
85	86	87	88	89	90	91	92	93	94	95	96
97	98	99	100	101	102	103	104	105	106	107	108
109	110	111	112	113	114	115	116	117	118	119	120

Abacus Evolve Year 4 Challenge PCM © Pearson Education Ltd 2009

Napier's bones

	0	1	2	3	4	5	6	7	8	9
1	0/0	0/1	0/2	0/3	0/4	0/5	0/6	0/7	0/8	0/9
2	0/0	0/2	0/4	0/6	0/8	1/0	1/2	1/4	1/6	1/8
3	0/0	0/3	0/6	0/9	1/2	1/5	1/8	2/1	2/4	2/7
4	0/0	0/4	0/8	1/2	1/6	2/0	2/4	2/8	3/2	3/6
5	0/0	0/5	1/0	1/5	2/0	2/5	3/0	3/5	4/0	4/5
6	0/0	0/6	1/2	1/8	2/4	3/0	3/6	4/2	4/8	5/4
7	0/0	0/7	1/4	2/1	2/8	3/5	4/2	4/9	5/6	6/3
8	0/0	0/8	1/6	2/4	3/2	4/0	4/8	5/6	6/4	7/2
9	0/0	0/9	1/8	2/7	3/6	4/5	5/4	6/3	7/2	8/1

Abacus Evolve Year 4 Challenge PCM © Pearson Education Ltd 2009

Fractions of a square

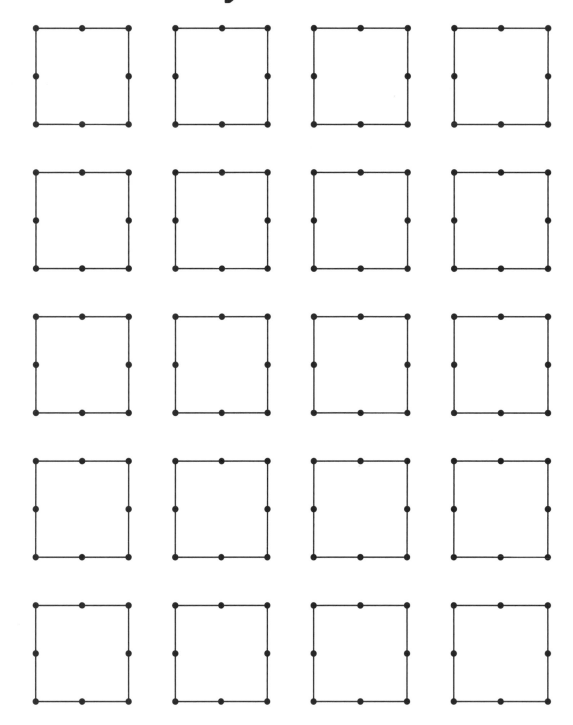

Abacus Evolve Year 4 Challenge PCM © Pearson Education Ltd 2009

Fractions and decimals link cards

A	B	C	D
2·5 Half of a fifth as a fraction	**2·5** Double $\frac{3}{4}$ as a decimal	**2·5** $\frac{1}{2} + \frac{1}{3} +$ what makes 1?	**2·5** A quarter of 11 as a mixed number
$\frac{1}{10}$ Double $\frac{4}{5}$ as a decimal	**1·5** A quarter of 2·5 as a fraction	$\frac{1}{6}$ $\frac{2}{5} +$ this makes $\frac{1}{2}$	$2\frac{3}{4}$ 2 divided by 12 as a fraction
1·6 2·75 as a mixed number	$\frac{5}{8}$ Half of 5·5 as a mixed number	$\frac{1}{10}$ Double $2\frac{1}{5}$ as a decimal	$\frac{1}{6}$ 9 times this fraction makes 3
$2\frac{3}{4}$ $\frac{1}{3}$ of 4·5 as a decimal	$2\frac{3}{4}$ Half of a half as a decimal	**4·4** $\frac{1}{2} + \frac{1}{8}$	$\frac{1}{3}$ $\frac{1}{10}$ of 2·5 as a decimal
1·5 $\frac{1}{6}$ of 2 as a fraction	**0·25** $\frac{1}{3}$ of 0·5 as a fraction	$\frac{5}{8}$ Four of these make 1	**0·25** 5 times this decimal makes 8
$\frac{1}{3}$ Half of 5 as a decimal	$\frac{1}{6}$ A quarter of 10 as a decimal	**0·25** Double $1\frac{1}{4}$	**1·6** $\frac{1}{8}$ of 20

Abacus Evolve Year 4 Challenge PCM © Pearson Education Ltd 2009

Abacus Evolve Year 4 Challenge PCM © Pearson Education Ltd 2009

Unit fractions of 12

You will need 12 counters.

Share all 12 counters into three equal groups.

 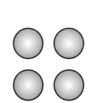

$\frac{1}{3}$ of 12 = _____

Share the counters into four equal groups. $\frac{1}{4}$ of 12 = _____

Two equal groups of _____ show that $\frac{1}{2}$ of 12   = _____

Six equal groups of _____ show that $\frac{1}{6}$ of 12   = _____

12 equal groups of _____ show that $\frac{1}{12}$ of 12   = _____

Use your findings to add these pairs of unit fractions.

$\frac{1}{2} + \frac{1}{3} =$ _____ $\frac{1}{3} + \frac{1}{12} =$ _____

$\frac{1}{4} + \frac{1}{6} =$ _____ $\frac{1}{2} + \frac{1}{6} =$ _____

Write the answers as twelfths. Can you change any of them into simpler fractions?

Abacus Evolve Year 4 Challenge PCM © Pearson Education Ltd 2009

Hamadi's camels

Before he died, Hamadi made his children promise to divide his camels between them like this:

Neema: $\frac{1}{2}$ Rashidi: $\frac{1}{4}$ Asim: $\frac{1}{8}$

When the children counted the camels, they found there were seven. They could not divide them as their father had asked.

Then the wise and respected Sharifa, a friend and neighbour, offered her help. "I will give you one of my camels," she said.

Hamadi's camels are the ones with the striped saddles.
Sharifa's camel is the one with the spotty saddle.

The eight camels could then be divided this like:

Neema: $\frac{1}{2}$ Rashidi: $\frac{1}{4}$ Asim: $\frac{1}{8}$

And Sharifa's camel could be given back to her!

How did this happen?

Make up your own story like this one, about a problem with fractions and a puzzling solution!

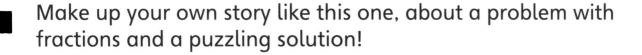

Egyptian fractions: investigation

How did the ancient Egyptians calculate fractions with a numerator of 2? (For example $\frac{2}{3}$, $\frac{2}{4}$, $\frac{2}{5}$ and $\frac{2}{6}$)

They split these fractions into unit fractions, starting with the largest possible unit fraction.

For example, they would split $\frac{2}{5}$ into $\frac{1}{3}$ and $\frac{1}{15}$.

This is how to split $\frac{2}{5}$ into unit fractions:

The largest unit fraction smaller than $\frac{2}{5}$ is $\frac{1}{3}$.
This means you need to work with thirds and fifths.
You will need 15 counters, because 15 is 3 × 5.

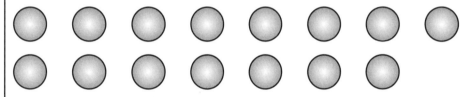

Start with $\frac{1}{3}$ of the counters.
$\frac{1}{3}$ of 15 is 5.

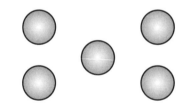

Our target is $\frac{2}{5}$. $\frac{2}{5}$ of 15 is 6.
We already have five counters, so we need one more.
One counter out of 15 is $\frac{1}{15}$.

So $\frac{2}{5}$ can be made by adding $\frac{1}{3}$ and $\frac{1}{15}$.

Use this method to find unit fractions which add to make other fractions with a numerator of 2. What patterns can you find?

If you have time, move on to fractions with a numerator of 3.

Abacus Evolve Year 4 Challenge PCM © Pearson Education Ltd 2009

Fraction number lines

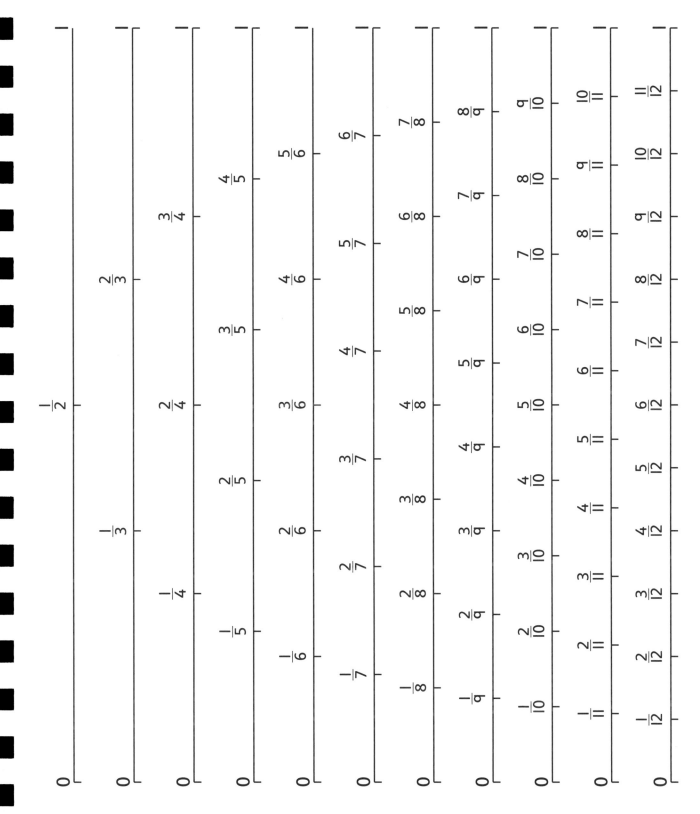

Abacus Evolve Year 4 Challenge PCM © Pearson Education Ltd 2009

Self-assessment sheet

	What I did to show this
I planned and completed my work in an organised way.	
I described patterns that I found.	
I made and tested predictions.	
I explained some of my findings, giving reasons.	
I wrote my conclusions looking back at my working.	
Other things I learned in this work.	

Abacus Evolve Year 4 Challenge PCM © Pearson Education Ltd 2009

Number walls

Put the numbers 1, 2 and 3 in the bottom row in different orders.
What is the largest possible top number? What is the smallest?

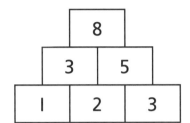 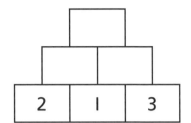 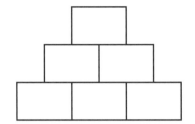

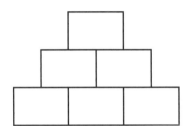 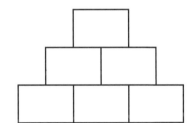 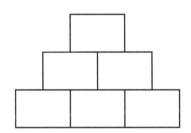

What happens if you put 2, 3 and 4 in the bottom row?

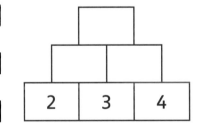 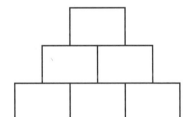 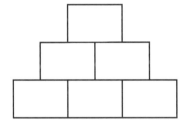

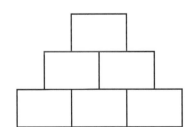 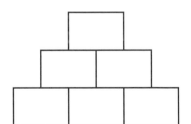 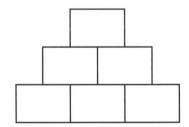

Use the blank number walls on PCM G to try other consecutive numbers on the bottom row. Investigate and write about any patterns that you see.

Abacus Evolve Year 4 Challenge PCM © Pearson Education Ltd 2009

Blank number walls

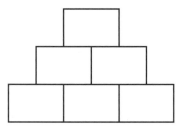 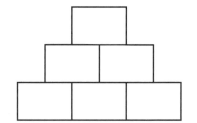 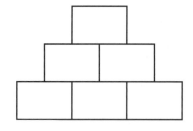

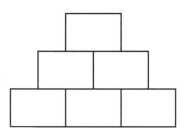 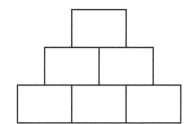 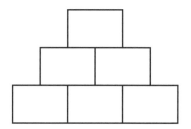

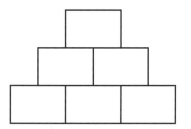 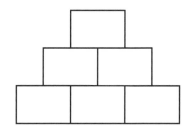 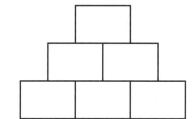

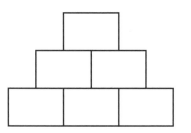 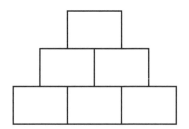 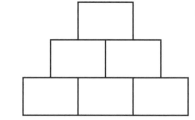

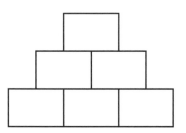 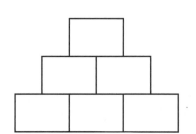 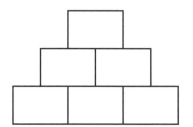

Abacus Evolve Year 4 Challenge PCM © Pearson Education Ltd 2009

Abacus Evolve Year 4 Challenge PCM © Pearson Education Ltd 2009

Building number walls

Find six different number walls with a top number of 10. Some have been started for you.

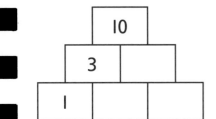 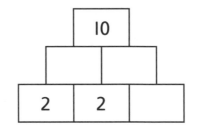 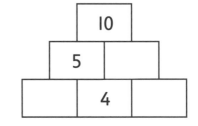

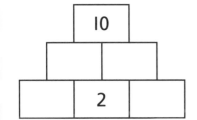 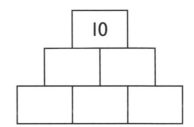 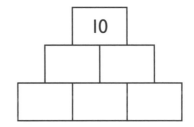

Now choose your own top number. Find as many different walls as you can with that top number.

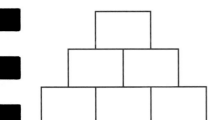 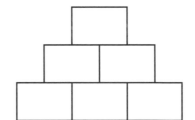 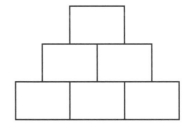

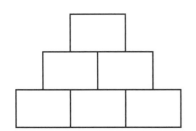 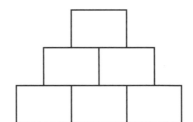 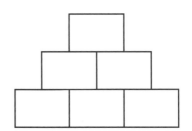

Continue your investigation using the blank walls on PCM G.

Hedra walls

Hedra walls are 3D number walls.

Cut out the first net. Write '12' on the top triangle. Complete each face of the hedra wall so it shows a different way of getting to 12. Can you make all six outer numbers (at the corners) different?

Glue the hedra wall together using the grey flaps.

Choose your own top number and made some more hedra walls.

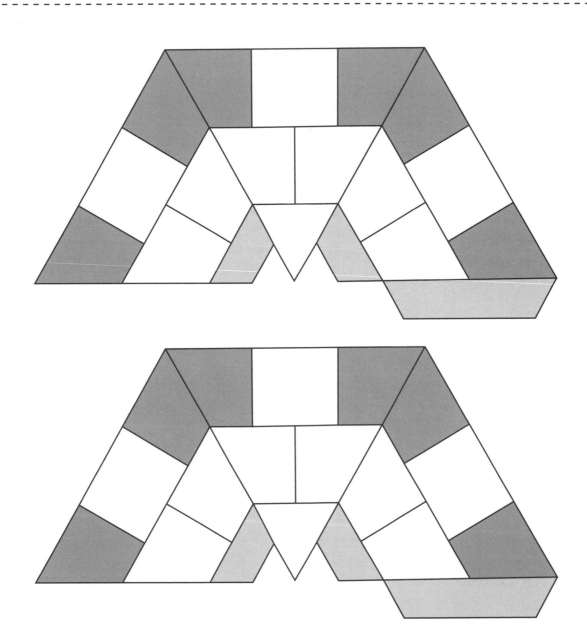

Abacus Evolve Year 4 Challenge PCM © Pearson Education Ltd 2009

Making shapes

What shapes can you make using this triangle and quadrilateral?

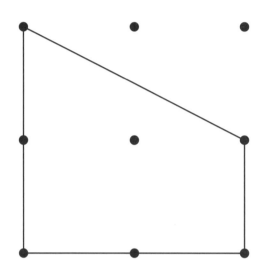 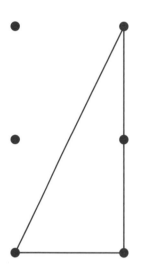

Describe each of the shapes you make.

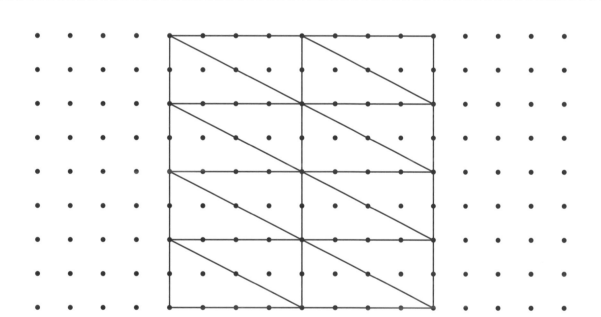

Abacus Evolve Year 4 Challenge PCM © Pearson Education Ltd 2009

Tessellation investigation

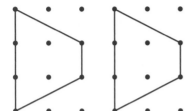

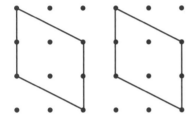

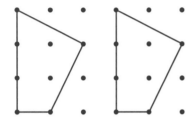

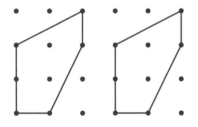

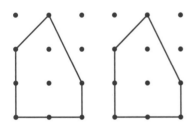

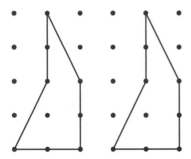

Abacus Evolve Year 4 Challenge PCM © Pearson Education Ltd 2009

Answers

A1

A1.1

1.

1	2	4
8	16	32
64	128	256
512	1024	2048
4096	8192	16 384
32 768	65 536	131 072
262 144	524 288	1 048 576
2 097 152	4 194 304	8 388 608
16 777 216	33 554 432	67 108 864
134 217 728	268 435 456	536 870 912

2. One thousand and twenty-four
   Two thousand and forty-eight
   Four thousand and ninety-six
   Eight thousand, one hundred and ninety-two
   Sixteen thousand, three hundred and eighty-four
   Thirty two thousand, seven hundred and sixty-eight
   Sixty five thousand, five hundred and thirty-six
   One hundred and thirty one thousand and seventy-two
   Two hundred and sixty two thousand, one hundred and forty-four
   Five hundred and twenty four thousand, two hundred and eighty-eight

Extra

Starting digit	The final digit pattern
1	1, 2, 4, 8, 6, 2, 4, 8, 6, 2 …
2	2, 4, 8, 6, 2, 4, 8, 6, 2 …
3	3, 6, 2, 4, 8, 6, 2 …
4	4, 8, 6, 2, 4, 8, 6, 2 …
5	5, 0, 0, 0 …
6	6, 2, 4, 8, 6, 2, 4, 8, 6, 2 …
7	7, 4, 8, 6, 2, 4, 8, 6, 2 …
8	8, 6, 2, 4, 8, 6, 2 …
9	9, 8, 6, 2, 4, 8, 6, 2 …

A1.2

1.

Roman	VII	XVII	XXIX	LXIV	CXLV	DCCVIII	MMMDCXX
Arabic	7	17	29	64	145	708	3620

Extra

A bar is added above a number to show 1000s, e.g.
$\overline{V} = 5000$,
$\overline{X} = 10\,000$

A1.3

1. A 3081, 3398
   B 3398, 3599, 3801, 4008
   C 3081, 3599, 3801
   D 3081, 3801, 4008
2. Answers will vary
3. Answers will vary
4. Answers will vary

Extra

For digits 1, 4, 5, 9 the possible numbers are (from smallest to largest reading down columns):

1459	4159	5149	9145
1495	4195	5194	9154
1549	4519	5419	9415
1594	4591	5491	9451
1945	4915	5914	9514
1954	4951	5941	9541

There will always be 24 possible combinations.
If one of the digits is 0 then pupils will need to decide if numbers are allowed to start with a 0; e.g. 0459

A1.4

1. 24
2. 32
3. 20
4. 15
5. $2 \times 5 \times 4 = 1 \times 10 \times 4 = 40$ (order of multiplication may be different)
6. $3 \times 3 \times 4 = 2 \times 3 \times 6 = 1 \times 3 \times 12 = 36$ (order of multiplication may be different)
7. $1 \times 10 \times 10 = 1 \times 2 \times 50 = 1 \times 4 \times 25 = 1 \times 5 \times 20 = 2 \times 2 \times 25 = 2 \times 5 \times 10 = 4 \times 5 \times 5 = 100$ (order of multiplication may be different)
8. Answers will vary.

Extra

If one of the three chosen digits is 2 then the product will always be even.
If one of the three chosen digits is 5 then the product will always end in 0 or 5 (it will be a multiple of 5)
If one of the three chosen digits is 2 and one is 5 then the product will always end in 0 (it will be a multiple of 10)

A1.5

PCM 1

1. Answers will vary, but should correctly partition 100, e.g.

×	3	7
10	30	70

2. Answers will vary, but should correctly partition 100, e.g.

×	10
3	30
7	70

3. Answers will vary, but should correctly partition 100, e.g.

×	4	6
3	12	18
7	28	42

AI.6

1. 16 boxes with 4 eggs left over
2. 8 boxes with 4 eggs left over
3. 10 boxes of 6 with 5 eggs left over; 5 boxes of 12 with 5 eggs left over
4. 13 boxes of 6 with 2 eggs left over; 6 boxes of 12 with 8 eggs left over
5. 19 boxes of 6 with 5 eggs left over; 9 boxes of 12 with 11 eggs left over
6. 4 red boxes (20) and 5 blue (40)
7. 5 red boxes (25) and 7 blue (56)
8. 12 red boxes (60) and 5 blue (40) or 4 red boxes (20) and 10 blue (80)

Extra

60 cereal bars: 7 boxes of seven and 1 box of 11
81 cereal bars: 10 boxes of seven and 1 box of 11
100 cereal bars: 8 boxes of seven and 4 boxes of 11

BI

BI.I

1. £446
2. £607
3. 3400
4. 7900
5. 27 000
6. 13 800
7. 100 000
8. 520 000
9. $6\frac{1}{2}$
10. $3\frac{1}{2}$
11. $2\frac{3}{4}$
12. $\frac{1}{4}$

Extra

$148 + 52 + 16 = 216$
$337 + 163 + 29 = 529$
$730 + 270 + 345 = 1345$
$681 + 319 + 112 = 1112$

BI.2

1. 8 kg
2. 34 kg
3. 264 g
4. A: 273 g, B: 278 g, C: 288 g, Total: 839 g

Extra

Answers will vary.

BI.3

PCM 2

Set A: 245 → 126 → 163 → 522 → 105 → 430
Set B: 245 → 105 → 1800 → 522 → 2050 → 815
Set C: 245 → 815 → 126 → 399 → 1800 → 2050
Set D: 245 → 522 → 815 → 430 → 2050 → 163

BI.4

PCM 3

1. There are eight possible solutions

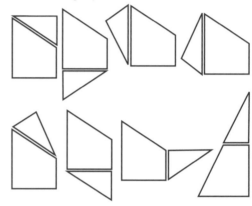

2. Pupils who found only four shapes will need to reflect the triangle to find the other four.
3. The rule is to fit the triangle and its reflection on each of the four sides of the trapezium.
4. Any other shapes will be rotations of the eight shapes above.
5. 1 triangle
6. 3 quadrilaterals
7. 4 pentagons
8. 0 hexagons
9. Shapes with more sides can be made if pupils do not have to match 2 sides of the same length.
10. Answers will vary. The total of all the angles will be 540° but some angles join to make 180° angles (i.e. straight lines).

Extra

Each shape will tesselate, e.g.

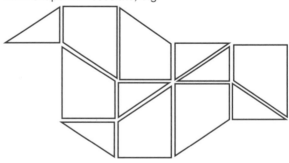

BI.5

PCM 4

1.

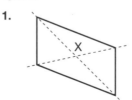

2. Three shapes have rotational symmetry.

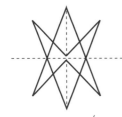 

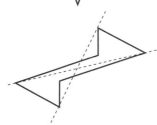

3. Shape b has no symmetry.

Extra

Answers will vary.

BI.6

PCM 5

1.

Orange triangle	Green triangle	Purple triangle
I have three different length sides. I have three different sized angles. I have a **right** angle.	I have three different length sides. I have three different sized angles. I have an <u>acute</u> angle.	I have three different length sides. I have three different sized angles. I have an <u>obtuse</u> angle.
My name is **right**-angled scalene triangle.	My name is <u>acute-angled</u> scalene triangle.	My name is <u>obtuse</u>-angled scalene triangle.

2.

Red triangle	Yellow triangle
I have just one line of symmetry. I have a right angle.	I have <u>just one line of symmetry</u>. I have all acute angles.
So, my name is right-angled isosceles triangle.	So, my name is <u>acute-angled</u> <u>isosceles triangle</u>.

Blue triangle	White triangle
I have <u>just one line of symmetry</u>. I have <u>an obtuse angle</u>.	I have <u>3 lines of symmetry</u>. All my angles <u>are the same length</u>. All my sides <u>are the same length</u>.
So, my name is <u>obtuse-angled isosceles</u> triangle.	So, my name is <u>equilateral triangle</u>.

3. Quadrilaterals: One square, one kite, one concave kite, one rectangle, one parallelogram, three trapeziums, four irregular quadrilaterals, one rhombus.

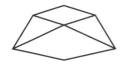
CI.I

1. 30 cm
2. 90 cm
3. 40 inches
4. 32 km
5. 160 km
6. 75 miles
7.

centimetres	5	30
inches	2	12

kilometres	8	32
miles	5	20

8. Answers will vary.

Extra

1 inch = 2·54 cm
1 mile = 1·609 km
1 ounce = 28·35 g
1 pint = 0·568 litres
1 pound = 0·454 kg

CI.2

1. **a** 10 cm **b** 10 cm **c** 10 cm **d** 8 cm **e** 10 cm
2. maximum perimeter = 18 cm
   minimum perimeter = 12 cm
   area always 8 cm²

Extra

maximum perimeter = 40 cm; minimum perimeter = 18 cm

CI.3

1.

Length (cm)	Width (cm)	Area (cm²)
1	2	2
2	3	6
3	4	12
4	5	20
5	6	30
6	7	42
7	8	56
8	9	72

2.

Length of side (cm)	Area (cm²)
1	1
2	4
3	9
4	16
5	25
6	36
7	49
8	64

3.

Length (cm)	Width (cm)	Area (cm²)
1	3	3
2	4	8
3	5	15
4	6	24
5	7	35
6	8	48
7	9	63
8	10	80

4. The area of a 1 by 3 rectangle is 1 unit less than the area of a square of side 2. A rectangle of perimeter p has an area 1 unit less than a square of the same perimeter.

Extra

Rectangles: The area of the L-shapes form the series of even numbers.

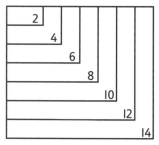

Squares: The area of the L-shapes form the series of odd numbers.

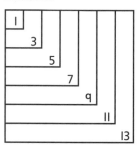

CI.4

PCM 7

1.

Small car	
Carbon cost (kg)	**Frequency**
0–9	1
10–19	4
20–29	3
30–39	4

Large car	
Carbon cost (kg)	**Frequency**
0–9	0
10–19	4
20–29	1
30–39	3
40–49	2
50–59	2

2.

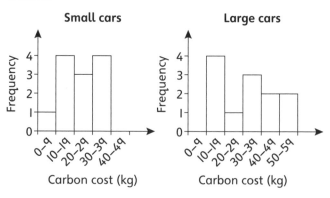

3.

Carbon cost (kg	Frequency
0–9	
10–19	
20–29	
30–39	
40–49	
50–59	

🚗 represents 1 car

4. and 5.

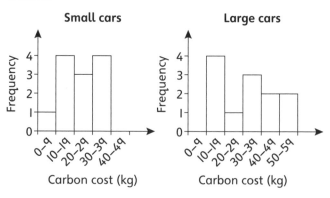

6. Answers will vary.

CI.5

PCM 8

Answers will vary.

CI.6

1.

Favourite puzzle	Frequency
Crosswords	6
Jigsaws	7
Codewords	4
Wordsearches	8
Sudoku	5

2.

Favourite puzzle	⚇ represents 2 people
Crosswords	3 figures
Jigsaws	3½ figures
Codewords	2 figures
Wordsearches	4 figures
Sudoku	2½ figures

3.

Favourite puzzle	⚇ represents 4 people
Crosswords	10 figures
Jigsaws	4½ figures
Codewords	3½ figures
Wordsearches	1 figure
Sudoku	6 figures

DI

DI.I

1. There are 24 ways of making 100	2. The opposite faces are:
5, 10, 85	95, 90, 15
5, 15, 80	95, 85, 20
5, 20, 75	95, 80, 25
5, 25, 70	95, 75, 30
5, 30, 65	95, 70, 35
5, 35, 60	95, 65, 40
5, 40, 55	95, 60, 45
5, 45, 50	95, 55, 45
10, 15, 75	90, 85, 25
10, 20, 70	90, 80, 30
10, 25, 65	90, 75, 35
10, 30, 60	90, 70, 40
10, 35, 55	90, 65, 45
10, 40, 50	90, 60, 50
15, 20, 65	85, 80, 35
15, 25, 60	85, 75, 40
15, 30, 55	85, 70, 45
15, 35, 50	85, 65, 50
15, 40, 45	85, 60, 55
20, 25, 55	80, 75, 45
20, 30, 50	80, 70, 50
20, 35, 45	80, 65, 55
25, 30, 45	75, 70, 55
25, 35, 40	75, 65, 60

3. The three hidden faces add up to 200. As each opposite pair adds to 100 and there are six faces, the total of all faces is 300. The visible faces also total 100 so $300 - 100 = 200$.

4. Answers will vary.

5. Answers will vary.

Extra

Answers will vary.

DI.2

1. The sum of two consecutive numbers is always odd.

2. The sum of three consecutive numbers can be odd or even; it is always divisible by 3 and equal to 3 × the middle number.

3. The sum of four consecutive numbers is always even. The sum of five consecutive numbers can be odd or even; it is always divisible by 5 and equal to 5 × the middle number.

The sum of six consecutive numbers is always odd and divisible by 3.

The sum of seven consecutive numbers can be odd or even; it is always divisible by 7 and equal to 7× the middle number.

The sum of eight consecutive numbers is always even and divisible by 4.

The sum of nine consecutive numbers can be odd or even; it is always divisible by 9 and equal to 9 × the middle number.

The sum of ten consecutive numbers is always odd and divisible by 5.

4. Rule: total $= a + (a + 1) + (a + 2) + (a + 3)$
$= 4a + 6$
$= 4 \times$ (first number) $+ 6$

5. Five consecutive numbers: total $= 5 \times$ (first number) $+ 10$

Six consecutive numbers: total $= 6 \times$ (first number) $+ 15$

Seven consecutive numbers: total $= 7 \times$ (first number) $+ 21$

etc.

6. $7 + 8 = 4 + 5 + 6 = 1 + 2 + 3 + 4 + 5 = 15$
$22 + 23 = 14 + 15 + 16 = 7 + 8 + 9 + 10 + 11 = 5 + 6 + 7 + 8 + 9 + 10 = 45$

Extra

Cannot make 4, 6, 8, 10, 12 or any even number.

DI.3

PCM 10

1. 70
2. 40
3. 50
4. 60
5. Answers will vary, e.g. $90 - 20 = 80 - 10$
6. Answers will vary, e.g. $100 - 10 = 70 + 20$
7. 69
8. 39
9. 81
10. 59
11. 98

12. 97
13. 100
14. 19, 19
15. 39, 39
16. 22, 22

DI.4

PCM II

1. Set A: 9:45 10:15 9:40 10:05 9:30 10:10
Set B: 9:45 10:05 9:35 10:25 9:55 10.20
Set C: 9:45 10:10 9:55 10:15 9:35 10:05
Set D: 9:45 10:25 9:30 10:20 9:40 10:15

DI.5

1. $\frac{1}{2} \rightarrow 30$
$\frac{1}{3} \rightarrow 20$
$\frac{2}{3} \rightarrow 40$
$\frac{1}{4} \rightarrow 15$
$\frac{1}{5} \rightarrow 12$
$\frac{1}{6} \rightarrow 10$
$\frac{1}{10} \rightarrow 6$
$\frac{5}{12} \rightarrow 25$
$\frac{1}{20} \rightarrow 3$
2. $\frac{3}{4} \rightarrow 45$
$\frac{3}{5} \rightarrow 36$
3. $18 \rightarrow \frac{3}{10}$
$5 \rightarrow \frac{1}{12}$

Extra

Answers will vary.
For example
$\frac{1}{3}$ of half an hour = 10 minutes
$\frac{1}{3}$ of two hours = 40 minutes

DI.6

PCM I3

1. 15°
2.

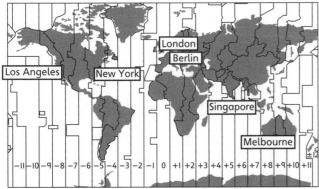

3. When you travel east, the local time is later than your body clock thinks it is. For example travelling from London, England to Melbourne, Australia. If the local time in Melbourne is 9pm, the flier will feel like it is 11am and may not be tired, even though it is bedtime. This is called jet lag.
4. Answers will vary.

EI

EI.I

1. 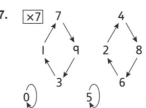 **2.**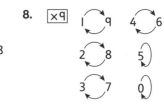

3. ×I **4.** ×5

5. ×3 **6.** ×6

7. ×7 **8.** ×q

Extra

Answers will vary.

EI.2

PCM I4

Answers will vary.

EI.3

PCM I5

2. 24, 30, 36, 40, 48, 60, 72, 80, 120, 144

3.

24	30	36	40	48	60	72	80	120	144
12 × 2	15 × 2	18 × 2	20 × 2	16 × 3	20 × 3	18 × 4	20 × 4	20 × 6	18 × 8
2 × 12	2 × 15	2 ×18	2 × 20	3 × 16	3 × 20	4 × 18	4 × 20	6 × 20	8 × 18
8 × 3	10 × 3	12 × 3	10 × 4	12 × 4	15 × 4	12 × 6	16 × 5	15 × 8	16 × 9
3 × 8	3 × 10	3 × 12	4 × 10	4 × 12	4 × 15	6 × 12	5 × 16	8 × 15	9 × 16
6 × 4	6 × 5	9 × 4	8 × 5	8 × 6	12 × 5	9 × 8	10 × 8	12 ×10	12 ×12
4 × 6	5 × 6	4 × 9	5 × 8	6 × 8	5 × 12	8 × 9	8 × 10	10 ×12	
		6 × 6			10 × 6				
					6 × 10				

1	2	3	4	5	6	7	8	9	10	11	12	13	14	15	16	17	18	19	20
2	4	6	8	10	12	14	16	18	20	22	24	26	28	30	32	34	36	38	40
3	6	9	12	15	18	21	24	27	30	33	36	39	42	45	48	51	54	57	60
4	8	12	16	20	24	28	32	36	40	44	48	52	56	60	64	68	72	76	80
5	10	15	20	25	30	35	40	45	50	55	60	65	70	75	80	85	90	95	100
6	12	18	24	30	36	42	48	54	60	66	72	78	84	90	96	102	108	114	120
7	14	21	28	35	42	49	56	63	70	77	84	91	98	105	112	119	126	133	140
8	16	24	32	40	48	56	64	72	80	88	96	104	112	120	128	136	144	152	160
9	18	27	36	45	54	63	72	81	90	99	108	117	126	135	144	153	162	171	180
10	20	30	40	50	60	70	80	90	100	110	120	130	140	150	160	170	180	190	200
11	22	33	44	55	66	77	88	99	110	121	132	143							
12	24	36	48	60	72	84	96	108	120	132	144								
13	26	39	52	65	78	91	104	117	130	143									
14	28	42	56	70	84	98	112	126	140										
15	30	45	60	75	90	105	120	135	150										
16	32	48	64	80	96	112	128	144	160										
17	34	51	68	85	102	119	136	153	170										
18	36	54	72	90	108	126	144	162	180										
19	38	57	76	95	114	133	152	171	190										
20	40	60	80	100	120	140	160	180	200										

4. Answers will vary. Pupils should appreciate that numbers with many factors will appear more frequently.

Extra

Square numbers have an odd number of multiplications.

EI.4

1.

10 × 3 = 30
5 × 6
$2\frac{1}{2} \times 12$
$1\frac{1}{4} \times 24$
$\frac{5}{8} \times 48$
$\frac{5}{16} \times 96$

18 × 5 = 90
9 × 10
$4\frac{1}{2} \times 20$
$2\frac{1}{4} \times 40$
$\frac{9}{8} \times 80$
$\frac{9}{16} \times 160$

14 × 6 = 84
7 × 12
$3\frac{1}{2} \times 24$
$1\frac{3}{4} \times 48$
$\frac{7}{8} \times 96$
$\frac{7}{16} \times 192$

2. Answers will vary.

3.

4 × 13 = 52
$8 \times 6\frac{1}{2}$
$16 \times 3\frac{1}{4}$

7 × 11 = 77
$14 \times 5\frac{1}{2}$
$28 \times 2\frac{3}{4}$

5 × 13 = 65
$10 \times 6\frac{1}{2}$
$20 \times 3\frac{1}{4}$

Extra

Answers will vary but should show that multiplying and dividing by the same number will give the same product as the original multiplication.

EI.5

1.
$1\frac{1}{2} + 8\frac{3}{5} = 10\frac{1}{10}$
$\frac{7}{8} + 9\frac{3}{8} = 10\frac{1}{4}$
$1\frac{3}{10} + 9\frac{1}{5} = 10\frac{1}{2}$
$\frac{3}{4} + 9\frac{7}{12} = 10\frac{1}{3}$
$1\frac{1}{3} + 8\frac{5}{6} = 10\frac{1}{6}$
$1\frac{1}{4} + 8\frac{7}{8} = 10\frac{1}{8}$
$\frac{5}{6} + 9\frac{1}{4} = 10\frac{1}{12}$
$\frac{1}{2} + 9\frac{7}{10} = 10\frac{1}{5}$

2.
$8\frac{3}{5} - \frac{1}{2} = 8\frac{1}{10}$
$9\frac{3}{8} - 1\frac{1}{4} = 8\frac{1}{8}$
$9\frac{1}{5} - \frac{3}{4} = 8\frac{9}{20}$
$9\frac{7}{12} - 1\frac{1}{2} = 8\frac{1}{12}$
$8\frac{5}{6} - \frac{5}{6} = 8$
$8\frac{7}{8} - \frac{7}{8} = 8$
$9\frac{7}{10} - 1\frac{3}{10} = 8\frac{2}{5}$
$9\frac{1}{4} - 1\frac{1}{3} = 7\frac{11}{12}$

Extra

Answers will vary.

EI.6

PCM 16

1.

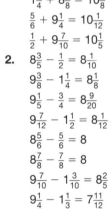

$\frac{1}{2} + \frac{1}{2} = 1$ $\frac{1}{6} + \frac{2}{3} + \frac{1}{6} = 1$ $\frac{1}{6} + \frac{2}{3} + \frac{1}{6} = 1$

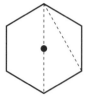

$\frac{1}{6} + \frac{5}{6} = 1$ $\frac{1}{2} + \frac{1}{3} + \frac{1}{6} = 1$ $\frac{1}{6} + \frac{1}{3} + \frac{1}{3} + \frac{1}{6} = 1$

2. Answers will vary but may include these shapes – some of the fraction sentences are beyond this level but are shown for completeness.

$\frac{1}{2} + \frac{1}{2} = 1$ $\frac{1}{3} + \frac{2}{3} = 1$ $\frac{1}{12} + \frac{11}{12} = 1$

$\frac{1}{12} + \frac{1}{4} + \frac{7}{12} = 1$ $\frac{1}{12} + \frac{5}{12} + \frac{1}{2} = 1$ $\frac{1}{12} + \frac{7}{12} + \frac{1}{3} = 1$

$\frac{1}{12} + \frac{5}{6} + \frac{1}{12} = 1$ $\frac{1}{3} + \frac{1}{6} + \frac{1}{2} = 1$ $\frac{1}{3} + \frac{1}{3} + \frac{1}{3} = 1$

A2

A2.I

1. Answers will vary.

2. Answers will vary.

3. Answers will vary.

4.

Set B	+200	−200	+2000	−2000	+20 000	−20 000
41 461	41 661	41 261	43 461	39 461	61 461	21 461
23 982	24 182	23 782	25 982	21 982	43 982	3982
35 980	36 180	35 780	37 980	33 980	55 980	15 980
66 312	66 512	66 112	68 312	64 312	86 312	46 312
19 875	20 075	19 675	21 875	17 875	39 875	−125
50 064	50 264	49 864	52 064	48 064	70 064	30 064
89 040	89 240	88 840	91 040	87 040	109 040	69 040
98 908	99 108	98 708	100 908	96 908	118 908	78 908
70 559	70 759	70 359	72 559	68 559	90 559	50 559

Set C	+500	−500	+5000	−5000	+50 000	−50 000
41 461	41 961	40 961	46 461	36 461	91 461	−8539
23 982	24 482	23 482	28 982	18 982	73 982	−26 018
35 980	36 480	35 480	40 980	30 980	85 980	−14 020
66 312	66 812	65 812	71 312	61 312	116 312	16 312
19 875	20 375	19 375	24 875	14 875	69 875	−30 125
50 064	50 564	49 564	55 064	45 064	100 064	64
89 040	89 540	88 540	94 040	84 040	139 040	39 040
98 908	99 408	98 408	103 908	93 908	148 908	48 908
70 559	71 059	70 059	75 559	65 559	120 559	20 559

Set D	+90	−90	+900	−900	+9000	−9000
41 461	41 551	41 371	42 361	40 561	50 461	32 461
23 982	24 072	23 892	24 882	23 082	32 982	14 982
35 980	36 070	35 890	36 880	35 080	44 980	26 980
66 312	66 402	66 222	67 212	65 412	75 312	57 312
19 875	19 965	19 785	20 775	18 975	28 875	10 875
50 064	50 154	49 974	50 964	49 164	59 064	41 064
89 040	89 130	88 950	89 940	88 140	98 040	80 040
98 908	98 998	98 818	99 808	98 008	107 908	89 908
70 559	70 649	70 469	71 459	69 659	79 559	61 559

Extra

Answers will vary.

A2.2

1. As a short-cut pupils could pair the numbers.
   50 × (1 + 100) = 5050
2. 145
3. 0
4. 100
5. 300
6. 220
7. 9, 10, 11, 12, 13, 14, 15
8. 11, 13, 15, 17, 19
9. 30, 32, 34

Extra

Answers will vary.

A2.4

PCM 18

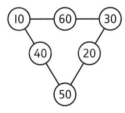

Numbers 10 – 60 give smallest total 90 and largest total 120.
Numbers 50, 100, 150, 200, 250, 300: possible totals are
450, 500, 550, 600.
Numbers 120, 150, 170, 200, 220, 250: a possible total is
540.

A2.5

PCM 19

1. 1
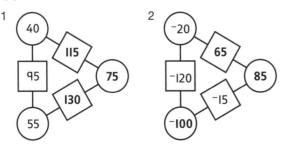

2. Add the 2 numbers in the squares and subtract
   2 × the number in the circle.

3.
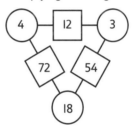

$a = \frac{1}{2}(b + d - e)$
$c = \frac{1}{2}(b + e - d)$
$f = \frac{1}{2}(d + e - b)$

Children can explain these patterns without using
algebra.

4. Answers will vary.

Extra

Multiplying arithmagon

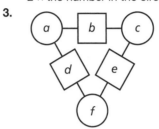

A2.6

PCM 20

1. 20
2. −15
3. Answers will vary.
   Game
   Set A: 0 → −25 → +15 → +50 → −20 → +14
   Set B: 0 → +14 → −20 → +50 → +15 → −25
   Set C: 0 → −28 → +32 → +14 → −12 → +64
   Set D: 0 → +64 → −12 → +14 → +32 → −28

Extra

Answers will vary.

B2.1

1. Pupils may produce two isosceles triangles, two
   rectangles or two trapeziums. In all cases the two
   pieces will be congruent.

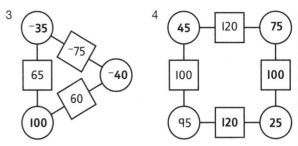

2. Rectangle: two congruent shapes, either right-angled triangle, rectangle or trapezium.
Rhombus: two congruent shapes, either isosceles triangle, parallelogram or trapezium
Parallelogram: two congruent shapes, either triangle, parallelogram or trapezium

3. Answers will vary.

Extra

Answers will vary.

B2.2

1.

1	2	3	4	5	6	7	8	9
2	~~4~~	6	~~8~~	10	~~12~~	14	~~16~~	18
4	~~8~~	12	~~16~~	20	~~24~~	28	~~32~~	36
~~8~~	16	24	32	40	48	56	64	72

Numbers left are all multiples of 2 (they are numbers from the 2 times-table).

Extra

Correct results for doubling to reach a 6-digit number

11	180 224
13	106 496
17	139 264
19	155 648
23	188 416 (not listed)
29	118 784

168 406 has no match

B2.3

1. The next set of steps uses 10 cubes.

2. The sequence continues
1, 3, 6, 10, 15, 21, 28, 36, 45, 55, 66, 78, 91, 106

3.

1	2	3	4	5	6	7	8	9	10
11	12	13	14	15	16	17	18	19	20
21	22	23	24	25	26	27	28	29	30
31	32	33	34	35	36	37	38	39	40
41	42	43	44	45	46	47	48	49	50
51	52	53	54	55	56	57	58	59	60
61	62	63	64	65	66	67	68	69	70
71	72	73	74	75	76	77	78	79	80
81	82	83	84	85	86	87	88	89	90
91	92	93	94	95	96	97	98	99	100

4. The difference between each number and the next is increasing by 1 each time.

Extra

Adding two adjacent triangle numbers gives a square number. If t_1 is the first triangular number then $t_1 + t_2 = 2^2$; $t_2 + t_3 = 3^2$; and $t_n + t_{n+1} = (n + 1)^2$

B2.4

PCM 22

Children's own constructions.

B2.5

PCM 23

1. *Prisms*

	Number of vertices	Number of edges	Number of faces
Triangular prism	**6**	9	**5**
Square prism	8	12	6
Pentagonal prism	10	15	7
Hexagonal prism	12	18	8
Decagonal prism	20	30	12

Patterns:
Number of vertices = 2 × number of sides of cross-section
Number of edges = 3 × number of sides of cross-section
Number of faces = number of sides of cross-section + 2

Pyramids

	Number of vertices	Number of edges	Number of faces
Triangular pyramid	**4**	**6**	**4**
Square pyramid	**5**	8	**5**
Pentagonal pyramid	6	10	6
Hexagonal pyramid	7	12	7
Decagonal pyramid	11	20	11

Patterns:
Number of vertices = number of sides of base + 1
Number of edges = 2 × number of sides of base
Number of faces = number of sides of base + 1 = number of vertices

PCM 24

	Number of triangles	Number of rectangles	Number of pentagons	Number of hexagons	Number of decagons
Triangular prism	2	3			
Square prism		6			
Pentagonal prism		5	2		
Hexagonal prism		6		2	
Decagonal prism		10			2
Triangular pyramid	4				
Square pyramid	4	1			
Pentagonal pyramid	5		1		
Hexagonal pyramid	6			1	
Decagonal pyramid	10				1

Extra

Answers will vary.

B2.6

1. There are 12 pentominoes

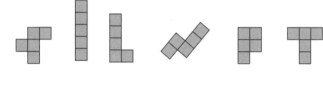

2. Open cubes can be made from these pentominoes.

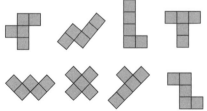

3. Children's own constructions.
4. Children add an extra square to the above nets to form any of the nets below.

5.

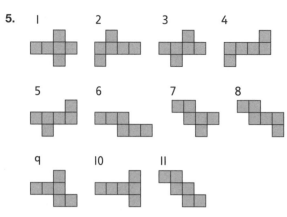

Extra

Rotational symmetry 3, 4, 6, 11
Line symmetry 1, 10
No symmetry 2, 5, 7, 8, 9

C2

C2.1

For example:

1. 4 steps

Step	B1	B2
fill B2	0	4
fill B1 from B2	1·5	2·5
empty B1	0	2·5
fill B1 from B2	1·5	**1**

2. 6 steps

Step	B1	B2
fill B2	0	2·5
fill B1 from B2	1·5	1
empty B1	0	1
empty B2 into B1	1	0
fill B2	1	2·5
top up B1 from B2	1·5	**2**

3. 8 steps

Step	B1	B2
fill B1	2	0
fill B2 from B1	0	2
fill B1	2	2
fill B2 from B1	1·5	2·5
empty B2	1·5	0
fill B2 from B1	0	1·5
fill B1	2	1·5
top up B2 from B1	**1**	2·5

4. 7 steps

Step	B1	B2
fill B2	0	4·5
fill B1 from B2	2	2·5
empty B1	0	2·5
fill B1 from B2	2	0·5
empty B1	0	0·5
fill B1 from B2	0·5	0
fill B2	**0·5**	**4·5**

B2

C2

191

5. 14 steps

Step	B1	B2	B3
fill B2	0	1·25	0
fill B1 from B2	0·75	0·5	0
fill B3 from B2	0·75	0	0·5
empty B1	0	0	0·5
fill B2	0	1·25	0·5
fill B1 from B2	0·75	0·5	0·5
fill B3 from B2	0·75	0	1
empty B1	0	0	1
fill B2	0	1·25	1
fill B1 from B2	0·75	0·5	1
empty B1	0	0·5	1
fill B1 from B2	0·5	0	1
fill B2	0·5	1·25	1
fill B1 from B2	0·75	**1**	**1**

6. 14 steps

Step	B1	B2	B3
			3·5
fill B1	1·5	0	3·5
fill B2 from B1	0	1·5	3·5
fill B2 from B3	0	2	3
empty B2	0	0	3
fill B1	1·5	0	3
fill B2 from B1	0	1·5	3
fill B2 from B3	0	2	2·5
fill B1 from B2	1·5	0·5	2·5
empty B1	0	0·5	2·5
fill B1 from B2	0·5	0	2·5
fill B2	0·5	2	2·5
fill B1 from B2	1·5	1	2·5
empty B1	0	1	2·5
fill B1 from B3	**1·5**	**1**	**1**

Extra

Answers will vary.

C2.2

1. About 70 pints
2. About 6 litres
3. 55
4. 90
5. 50
6. 15

Extra

Answers will vary.

C2.3

1. 1 h 21 min; 46 min; 46 min; 10 min. Train 5 arrives 31min after 09:00
2. 6 min and 4 min
3. 1h 37 min; 1 h 42 min; 1 h 27 min; 1 h 33 min; 1 h 24 min

4. Train 5
5. Train 3 (revised arrival time 08:44)
6. 07:00 or 10:30
7. Leave home 09:25, arrive airport 09:50, flight 10:30, land 11:25; collect baggage 11:55; arrive restaurant 12:25; 14:30–17:45 explore Belfast; 17:50 go to airport; arrive airport 18:20; flight 19:00, land 19:55; collect baggage 20:25; arrive home 20:50
8. Answers will vary.
9. Answers will vary.

Extra

Quickest route Stansted → Manchester → Belfast. Flight time 90 min.

C2.4

PCM 27

Perimeter	Area	Side 1	Side 2
26 cm	42 cm²	6 cm	7 cm
28 cm	49 cm²	7 cm	7 cm
30 cm	44 cm²	4 cm	11 cm
24 cm	20 cm²	2 cm	10 cm
20 cm	24 cm²	6 cm	4 cm
24 cm	36 cm²	6 cm	6 cm
26 cm	36 cm²	4 cm	9 cm
42 cm	90 cm²	6 cm	15 cm

Lengths of sides 1 and 2 may be transposed.

Perimeter	Short side length	Long side length
15 cm	2 cm	3 cm
21 cm	1 cm	6 cm
24 cm	2 cm	6 cm
27 cm	4 cm	5 cm

Shape 1 – 20 cm²
Shape 2 – 84 cm²
Shape 3 – 15 cm²

C2.5

1. Largest area: 7·5 cm × 7·5 cm. Area 56·25 cm²
2. Area nearest to 20 cm²: 13·5 cm × 1·5 cm. Area 20·25 cm²
3. Smallest area: 14·5 cm × 0·5 cm. Area 7·25 cm²
4. There are many possible shapes. Minimum area 14 square units, maximum 56 square units.

Extra

Maximum area 112 triangles, minimum area 28 triangles.

C2.6

1. Raw data

Walking	1,2,5,3,1,2,5,2,3,4, 0,2,1,2,1,1,0,3,3,0 4,6,3,2,4,5,3,4,6,3, 3,3,4,2,3,3,4,3,2,3
Bicycle	*4,3,1,0,5,3,1,4,2,2, 0,0,0,0,0,0,0,0,0,0, 0,0,2,2,2,2,2,0,0,2, 3,4,1,1,1,1,1,4,4,1*
Bus	0,1,0,2,3,3,1,0,0,2, 0,2,2,0,0,2,0,2,0,0, 0,0,0,0,0,0,0,0,0,0, 0,0,0,2,0,0,2,0,0,0
Train	0,0,0,2,0,0,0,0,0,2, 0,2,0,0,0,2,0,0,0,0, 2,0,0,0,0,0,0,2,0,0, 0,0,2,0,2,2,0,0,0,2
Car	2,0,2,1,1,2,1,2,1,0, 6,4,4,6,6,4,2,3,2,4, 2,2,0,0,2,0,2,2,2,0, 1,3,4,1,2,0,0,3,2,1

Grouped data

	0	1	2	3	4	5	6
Walking	3	5	8	13	6	3	2
Bicycle	15	8	8	3	5	1	0
Bus	28	2	8	2	0	0	0
Train	30	0	10	0	0	0	0
Car	8	7	14	3	5	0	3

2. Answers will vary.
3. Answers will vary.
4. Answers will vary.
5. Answers will vary.

D2

D2.1

Questions 1–4: There are other correct solutions.
1. $872 + 964 = 1836$
   $269 + 748 = 1017$
   $28 + 74 + 96 = 198$
2. $405 + 826 = 1231$
   $526 + 480 = 1006$
   $42 + 58 + 60 = 160$
3. $847 + 153 = 1000$
   $148 + 357 = 505$
   $17 + 38 + 45 = 100$
4. $697 + 805 = 1502$
   $598 + 607 = 1205$
   $59 + 67 + 80 = 206$

Extra

Lowest possible score 3. For example $401 - 398 = 3$

D2.2

1. 11, 22, 33, 44, 55, 66, 77, 88, 99; all in the 11 times-table.
2. Answers will vary.

D2.3

1. £4·93
2. £6·32 − £1·51 = £4·81
   £6·24 − £1·49 = £4·75
   £6·48 − £1·66 = £4·82
   £6·30 − £1·54 = £4·76
   £6·45 − £1·52 = £4·93
   £6·19 − £1·42 = £4·77
   £6·43 − £1·59 = £4·84
   £6·22 − £1·43 = £4·79
   £6·49 − £1·61 = £4·88
3. Answers will vary.

D2.4

1. 306
2. 633
3. £3·46
4. £7·81
5. 1 m 68 cm
6. 8 m 12 cm
7. The difference will always be the same. This works for all numbers.

Extra

184 and 320

D2.5

1, 2 and 3

	Amie	Bart	Chan	**Total**
Starter	Oysters $30.50	Pepper soup $34.90	Taster plate £48.50	$113.90
Main	Kingfish $64.90	Goat's cheese $48.90	Steak $72.50	$186.30
Dessert	Bread pudd $28.50	Cheese $48.00	Taster plate $46.90	$123.40
Total	$123.90	$131.80	$167.90	**$423.60**

Extra

Bart had speciality tea.

	Amie	Bart	Chan	**Total**
Starter	Oysters $30.50	Pepper soup $34.90	Taster plate £48.50	$113.90
Main	Kingfish $64.90	Goat's cheese $48.90	Steak $72.50	$186.30
Dessert	Bread pudd $28.50	Cheese $48.00	Taster plate $46.90	$123.40
Drink	China tea $18.90	Speciality tea $22.50	Coffee $20.50	$61.90
Total	$142.80	$154.30	$188.40	**$485.50**

D2.6

PCMs 32 and 33

Highest possible score – one correct permutation

5	2	1	521
8	4	3	+ 843
9	7	6	+ 976
			= 2340
589	+247	+136	= 972
2340 − 972 = 1368			

E2

E2.1

PCM 34

1

24 × 9	
24	9
48	4
96	2
192	1
216	

2

35 × 12	
35	12
70	6
140	3
280	1
420	

3

23 × 14	
23	14
46	7
92	3
184	1
322	

Corrected charts

4

27 × 13	
27	13
54	6
108	3
216	1
27 + 108 + 216 = 351	

5

21 × 19	
21	19
42	9
84	4
168	2
336	1
21 + 42 + 336 = 399	

6

29 × 16	
29	16
58	8
116	4
232	2
464	1
464	

Extra

25 × 15	
25	15
50	7
100	3
200	1
25 + 50 + 100 + 200 = 375	
375 ÷ 25 = 15	

E2.2

1. 23 × 4 = 92   24 × 3 = 72
   32 × 4 = 128   34 × 2 = 64
   42 × 3 = 126   43 × 2 = 86
   Maximum product 32 × 4 = 128
2. 32 × 5 = 160
3. 43 × 5 = 215
4. 43 × 9 = 387

5. 82 × 9 = 738
   Single-digit number is always the largest, 2-digit number has larger digit in 10s column.
6. For example 1, 2, 3, 4 maximum product
   41 × 32 = 1312
   Two largest digits in the 10s column. Units column has smallest digit paired with largest 10s digit.
   For example 3, 5, 7, 9 max product from 9 with 3 and 7 with 5; 93 × 75 = 6975

E2.3

PCM 35

1. 9 × 50p = £4·50
   90 cm × 5 = 4 m 50 cm
   90 × 5 = 450
   450 ÷ 5 = 90
   450 ÷ 9 = 50
   9 × 50 = 450

   8 × 70p = £5·60
   70 cm × 8 = 5 m 60 cm
   70 × 8 = 560
   7 × 80 = 560
   560 ÷ 8 = 70
   56 ÷ 8 =7
   56 ÷ 7 = 8
   560 ÷ 7 = 80
   70 × 8 = 560
2. 40 × 32 = 1280
3. 33 × 60 = 1980
4. 20 × 28 = 1400
5. 26 × 30 = 780
6. 70 × 24 = 1680
7. 13 × 90 = 1170

Extra

41 × 32 = 1312   40 × 33 = 1320
34 × 60 = 2040   33 × 61 = 2013
51 × 28 = 1428   50 × 29 = 1450
27 × 30 = 810   26 × 31 = 806
71 × 24 = 1704   70 × 25 = 1750
14 × 90 = 1260   13 × 91 = 1183
30 × 26 = 780 then 31 × 26 = 780 + 26 (= 806) and
30 × 27 = 780 + 30 (= 810)

E2.4

17 camels means you cannot divide exactly in half; adding 1 to make 18 makes an amount that can be divided by 2, 3 and 9:

18 ÷ 2 = 9
18 ÷ 3 = 6
18 ÷ 9 = 2
9 + 6 + 2 = 17 so 1 camel left over can be returned

1. This sharing problem will work with any number that is a multiple of 2, 6 and 9.
2. Answers will vary. The denominators of the fractions used to share must be factors of the number of camels.
3. Answers will vary.

Extra

$\frac{1}{2}$ of 24 = 12

The total number of camels is found by multiplying the denominator of the fraction by the number of camels in your share.

E2.5

PCM 36

1.

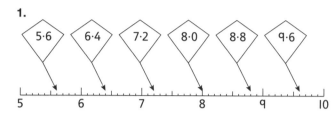

Kite card game in ascending order

5·1
53 tenths = 5·3
11 halves = 5·5
59 tenths = 5·9
$6\frac{1}{5}$ = 6·2
6·8
76 tenths = 7·6
7·9
81 tenths = 8·1
17 halves = 8·5
$9\frac{1}{5}$ = 9·2
95 tenths = 9·5

Ladder cards in ascending order

15 fifths = 3
31 tenths = 3·1
3·2
$3\frac{1}{4}$ = 3·25
3·3
34 tenths = 3·4
7 halves = 3·5
$3\frac{1}{2}$ = 3·5
3·5
36 tenths = 3·6
3·7
$3\frac{3}{4}$ = 3·75
3·8
39 tenths = 3·9
20 fifths = 4

E2.6

PCM 38

Set A: 42 → 1·6 → 52 → 10·5 → 36 → 2·4

Set B: 10·5 → 58 → 52 → 2·9 → 81 → 2·4

Set C: 81 → 42 → 39 → 58 → 2·9 → 2·4

Set D: 52 → 81 → 36 → 2·9 → 1·6 → 2·4

A3

A3.1

PCM 39

Nearest 10

£20 → £40 → £50 → £60 → £30 → £70

£30 → £50 → £60 → £40 → £20 → £70

£60 → £20 → £50 → £30 → £40 → £70

£40 → £30 → £20 → £50 → £60 → £70

PCM 40

Nearest 5

£115 → £110 → £95 → £105 → £90 → £100

£90 → £95 → £105 → £110 → £115 → £100

£105 → £115 → £95 → £90 → £110 → £100

£110 → £90 → £115 → £95 → £105 → £100

A3.2

1.

×	9	$\frac{1}{2}$
7	63	$3\frac{1}{2}$
$\frac{1}{2}$	$4\frac{1}{2}$	$\frac{1}{4}$

$9\frac{1}{2} \times 7\frac{1}{2} = 71\frac{1}{4}$

2.

×	10	0·4
8	80	3·2
0·4	4	0·16

$8·4 \times 10·4 = 87·36$

	Minimum perimeter	Maximum perimeter	Minimum area	Maximum area
3.	26 cm	29·6 cm	41·25 cm²	53·76 cm²
4.	30 cm	34·6 cm	55·25 cm²	69·56 cm²
5.	38 cm	41·6 cm	89·25 cm²	107·16 cm²
6.	42 cm	45·6 cm	109·25 cm²	128·96 cm²
7.	46 cm	49·6 cm	131·25 cm²	152·76 cm²
8.	50 cm	53·6 cm	155·25 cm²	178·56 cm²

Extra

Lengths to the nearest $\frac{1}{2}$ cm

Lengths	min 9·75 cm	max 10·2 cm
Perimeter	min 39 cm	max 40·8 cm
Area (2dp)	min 95·06 cm²	max 104·04 cm²

Lengths to the nearest 2 mm

Lengths	min 9·9 cm	max 10·1 cm
Perimeter	min 39·6 cm	max 40·4 cm
Area	min 98·01 cm²	max 102·01 cm²

Lengths to the nearest 1 mm

Lengths	min 9·95 cm	max 10·04 cm
Perimeter	min 39·8 cm	max 40·16 cm
Area (2dp)	min 99·00 cm²	max 100·80 cm²

A3.3

PCM 41

1.

10 000 000	20 000 000	30 000 000	40 000 000	50 000 000	60 000 000	70 000 000	80 000 000	90 000 000
1 000 000	2 000 000	3 000 000	4 000 000	5 000 000	6 000 000	7 000 000	8 000 000	9 000 000
100 000	200 000	300 000	400 000	500 000	600 000	700 000	800 000	900 000
10 000	20 000	30 000	40 000	50 000	60 000	70 000	80 000	90 000
1000	2000	3000	4000	5000	6000	7000	8000	9000
100	200	300	400	500	600	700	800	900
10	20	30	40	50	60	70	80	90
1	2	3	4	5	6	7	8	9
0·1	0·2	0·3	0·4	0·5	0·6	0·7	0·8	0·9
0·01	0·02	0·03	0·04	0·05	0·06	0·07	0·08	0·09
0·001	0·002	0·003	0·004	0·005	0·006	0·007	0·008	0·009
0·0001	0·0002	0·0003	0·0004	0·0005	0·0006	0·0007	0·0008	0·0009
0·000 01	0·000 02	0·000 03	0·000 04	0·000 05	0·000 06	0·000 07	0·000 08	0·000 09

3. Move down a row on the chart.
4. Multiply by moving up 2 rows, divide by moving down 2 rows.
5. Answers will vary.
6. Answers will vary.

Extra

Multiply by 5 and then use the chart to multiply your answer by 10 and 100.

A3.4

PCM 42

1.

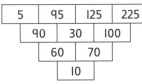 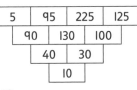

Bottom brick will always be 10.

2.

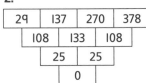 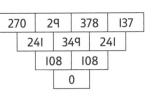

Bottom brick will always be 0.

3. Answers will vary. For example:

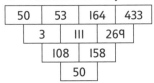 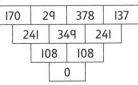

4. Answers will vary. For example:

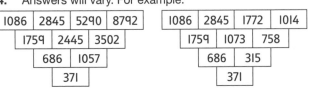

5. Answers will vary. For example:

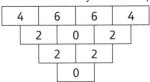

6. Answers will vary. For example:

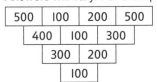

7. Answers will vary. For example answer to question 6.
8. Answers will vary.

Extra

Answers will vary but the bottom brick will always be 0. For example:

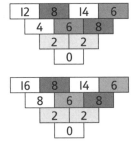

A3.5

1. 148 to 216 = 68; 218 − 150 = 68; 118 − 50 = 68
2. Add 13. 405 − 187 = 418 − 200 = 218
3. 341 − 198 = 343 − 200 = 143
4. 229 − 152 = 227 − 150 = 77
5. 807 − 529 = 808 − 530 = 278
6. 753 − 395 = 758 − 400 = 358

PCM 43

905 − 677 = 228	977 − 749 = 228
725 − 457 = 268	817 − 549 = 268
635 − 347 = 288	737 − 449 = 288
545 − 237 = 308	657 − 349 = 308
455 − 127 = 328	527 − 199 = 328
902 − 544 = 358	908 − 550 = 358
803 − 455 = 348	798 − 450 = 348
704 − 366 = 338	688 − 350 = 338
605 − 277 = 328	628 − 300 = 328
407 − 99 = 308	408 − 100 = 308
933 − 589 = 344	919 − 575 = 344
844 − 489 = 355	830 − 475 = 355
666 − 289 = 377	652 − 275 = 377
577 − 189 = 388	563 − 175 = 388
488 − 89 = 399	474 − 75 = 399

A3.6

1. 321 − 123 = 198   432 − 234 = 198
   543 − 345 = 198
   Answer always 198. In the first number the hundreds digit is always 200 more and the units digit is 2 less. 200 − 2 = 198. (Algebraic proof leads to 99 × 2.)
2. Answers always 396 (99 × 4) for both odd and even digits.
3. 594 (99 × 6)
4. 3087 (3000 + 100 − 10 − 3)
5. £2.22, (£2 + 20p + 2p)
6. £22.22 (£20 + £2 + 20p + 2p)

Extra

Answers will vary. For example:
513111 − 111315 = 401796
715131 − 131517 = 583614
917151 − 151719 = 765432
Each total increases by 181818

B3

B3.I

1. As long as the answer to the subtraction has 3 digits it will always give 1089. If the answer to the subtraction is 99 then the answer is 198, e.g. 231 − 132 = 99 and 99 + 99 = 198.
   e.g. 9876 − 6789 = 3087 → 8730 − 0378 = 8352 → 8532 − 2358 = 6174
2. 6174 → 7641 − 1467 = 6174

Extra

2-digit numbers sequence e.g.
21 − 12 = 9 → 9 + 9 = 18
31 − 13 = 18 → 18 + 81 = 99
41 − 14 = 27 → 72 + 27 = 99
85 − 58 = 27 → 72 + 27 = 99
If the subtraction ends in a single digit then sequence ends at 18, otherwise it ends at 99.

4-digit numbers sequence e.g.
4321 − 1234 = 3087 → 3087 + 7803 = 10890
9321 − 1239 = 8082 → 8082 + 2808 = 10890
2001 − 1002 = 999 → 999 + 999 = 1998
If the subtraction ends in a 2-digit number then sequence ends at 1998, otherwise it ends at 10890.

B3.2

PCM 44

1. Answers will vary.
2.

Set A	Set B
121 × 18 = 2178	414 ÷ 18 = 23
29 × 81 = 2349	432 ÷ 24 = 18
55 × 45 = 2475	468 ÷ 36 = 13
143 × 18 = 2574	486 ÷ 18 = 27
289 × 9 = 2601	522 ÷ 18 = 29
33 × 81 = 2673	540 ÷ 45 = 12
153 × 18 = 2754	558 ÷ 18 = 31
313 × 9 = 2817	576 ÷ 36 = 16
46 × 63 = 2898	612 ÷ 36 = 17
65 × 45 = 2925	630 ÷ 30 = 21

Extra

× 1	1089	× 1	9109
× 2	2178	× 2	18 218
× 3	3267	× 3	27 327
× 4	4356	× 4	36 436
× 5	5445	× 5	45 545
× 6	6534	× 6	54 654
× 7	7623	× 7	63 763
× 8	8712	× 8	72 872
× 9	9801	× 9	81 981
× 10	10 890	× 10	91 090

Answers will vary but may include:
1089 table
1000s digit goes from 1 to 10
100s digit goes from 0 to 9
10s digit goes 8, 7, 6, … 0, 9
Units digit goes from 9 to 0

9109 table
All have pattern [9 × pattern number] [pattern number] [9 × pattern number]
So 9109 × 3 = [9 × 3] [3] [9 × 3] = 27327

B3.3

1. 1000 dr 1   25 × 40 dr 7 × 4 = 28 → 1
2. 391 dr 4   23 × 17 dr 5 × 8 40 → 4
3. 1540 dr 1   44 × 35 dr 8 × 8 = 64 → 1
4. 1078 dr 7   98 × 11 dr 8 × 2 = 16 → 7
5. 24 dr 6   8 × 24 dr 6 × 8 = 48 → 3   192 dr 3
6. 25 dr 7   7 × 25 dr 7 × 7 = 49 → 4   175 dr 4
7. 14 dr 5   16 × 14 dr 5 × 7 = 35 → 8   224 dr 8
8. 19 dr 1   21 × 19 dr 1 × 3 = 3   339 dr 3

0 dr 0	1 dr 1	2 dr 2	3 dr 3	4 dr 4	5 dr 5	6 dr 6	7 dr 7	8 dr 8
9 dr 9	10	11	12	13	14 dr 5	15	16	17
18	19	20	21	22	23 dr5	24	25	26
27	28	29	30	31	32 dr 5	33	34	35
36	37	38	39	40	41 dr 5	42	43	44
45	46	47	48	49	50 dr 5	51	52	53
54	55	56	57	58	59 dr 5	60	61	62
63	64	65	66	67	68 dr 5	69	70	71
72	73	74	75	76	77 dr 5	78	79	80
81	82	83	84	85	86 dr 5	87	88	89
90	91	92	93	94	95 dr 5	96	97	98

When you divide numbers by 9 the remainder is equal to the digital root.

Note: 0 has a digital root 0.

B3.4

1. S
2. W
3. 135°
4. 315°
5. 225°
6. 157·5°
7. 022·5°
8. 247·5°
9. 337·5°
10. 112·5°
11. 067·5°
12. 11·5 km from both lookouts.

B3.5

Answers will vary.

B3.6

Angles constructed are 90°, 45°, 135°
1. As the angle sum of all polygons is a multiple of 180 any may be constructed using the angles given.
2. Angle sum = 180 × (number of sides − 2)

C3

C3.1

1. Answers will vary. Shortest possible route is three radial roads from the circumcentre of the triangle. For the equilateral triangle shown the total length of road is 173 km; for the right-angled triangle it is 194 km.

2. Answers will vary. Shortest route is 4 radial roads from the centre of the square. Total length is 283 km.

Extra

Answers will vary. For any rhombus the minimum distance will be roads from the centre.

C3.2

PCM 47

1. (2,3)
2. (4,3)
3. 3 cm or 30 mm
4. 40 m
5. (3,4)
6. (3,1)
7. 4·5 cm or 45 mm
8. 60 m

C3.3

1. All values rounded to nearest 5 (or nearest million)

Object	Mass (kg)	Approximate weight (N) on:			
		Earth	Mars	Moon	Titan
A child	30	300	115	50	30
A bicycle	15	150	55	25	15
A family car	1 250	12 500	4690	2080	1250
A lorry	2 000	20 000	7500	3330	2000
Eiffel Tower	8 million	80 million	30 million	13 million	8 million

2. Answers will vary.

Extra

Body	Gravity compared to Earth's (approx.)
Sun	30
Mercury	0·4
Venus	0·9
Earth	1·0
Moon	0·2
Mars	0·4
Jupiter	2·6
Saturn	1·1
Uranus	1·1
Neptune	1·4
Pluto	0·04

C3.4

1.

	Start time	Half-time break	Predicted arrival time
1	9 am	10:47 – 10:57 am	12:44 pm
2	10:15 am	12:48 – 12:58 pm	3:31 pm
3	11:30 am	12:44 – 12:54 pm	2:08 pm
4	12:45 pm	3:50 – 4:00 pm	7:05 pm

2.

	Start time	Journey duration	Time when fraction of journey left			
			Half	Third	Quarter	Tenth
1	9 am	3 h 44 min	10:52 am	11:29 am	11:48 am	12:34 pm
2	10:15 am	5 h 16 min	12:53 pm	1:46 pm	2:12 pm	3:00 pm
3	11:30 am	2 h 38 min	12:49 pm	1:15 pm	1:28 pm	1:52 pm
4	12:45 pm	6 h 20 min	3:55 pm	4:58 pm	5:30 pm	6:27 pm

C3.5

Carroll diagram shows numbers from 1 to 20 grouped by odd/even and <10/⩾10.
Venn diagram shows subsets of odd numbers <20 and numbers ⩽20.

1. Answers will vary. For example:
For numbers 10 to 20

	Multiple of 5	Not multiple of 5
Even digital root	15 20	11 13 15 17
Odd digital root	10	12 14 16 18 19

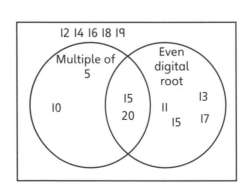

2.

	2 lines of symmetry	Not 2 lines of symmetry
Pair of parallel sides	rectangle, rhombus	square, parallelogram, trapezium
No parallel sides		irregular quadrilateral, kite, arrowhead (concave kite)

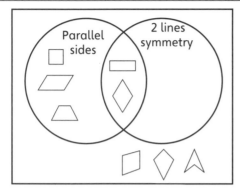

Extra

Pupils should attempt a Venn diagram with three circles.

C3.6

Answers will vary but sets are as follows.

Numbers
Even {84, 88, 90, 96, 100, 104, 108, 120}
Multiples of 5 {75, 90, 100, 105, 120}
Square numbers {81, 100, 121}
Digital root a multiple of 3 {75, 81, 84, 90, 96, 99, 105, 108, 111, 120}

Shapes
Quadrilateral {square, rectangle, kite, arrowhead, rhombus, parallelogram, isosceles trapezium, right-angled trapezium}
Has a right-angle {right-angled scalene triangle, right-angled isosceles triangle, square, rectangle, right-angled trapezium}
At least 2 lines of symmetry {pentagon, square, rectangle, rhombus}
At least 1 pair parallel sides {square, rectangle, rhombus, parallelogram, isosceles trapezium}
Only 2 different angle sizes {isosceles triangles, right-angled isosceles triangle, rhombus, parallelogram, isosceles trapezium}

D3

D3.1

1. Amir's number is 50, Becky's number is 30 and Chris's number is 70.
2. 186, 192, 204
3. Answers will vary.
4. Answers will vary.
5. A 64   B 35   C 47
6. A £6.90   B £5.70   C £5.80
7. A £43   B £29   C £31   D £25
8. A 572   B 619   C 483   D 398

D3.2

Answers will vary. Correct solutions given.
1. 135   2. £4·50
3. 435   4. £23·25

5. 63   6. £5·93
7. £8·90   8. £26·78
9. £43·58   10. £57·76

D3.3

PCM 48

1. Socks; evening dress; plain white shirt
2. Men's suit
3. Men's golf shorts; denim shorts
4. Striped jumper; women's golf shorts
5. High heels
6. T-shirt; sunhat; baseball cap; men's blazer; plain white polo shirt
7. About $\frac{1}{10}$ off: pocket detail shirt; jeans; black polo shirt; polo neck jumper

Extra

	Sale price	£15	£24	£10	£8	£30
Original price if	half-price	£30	£48	£20	£16	£60
	$\frac{1}{3}$ off	£22.50	£36	£15	£12	£45
	$\frac{1}{4}$ off	£20	£32	£13.33	£10.67	£40
	10% off	£16.67	£26.67	£11.11	£8.89	£33.33

D3.4

1. The distance between each number decreases up the number line.
2. 16   3. 25
4. 36   5. 18
6. 9   7. 8
8. 8   9. 7

Extra

To calculate larger or smaller numbers you can use known facts. For example $4 \times 9 = 36 \rightarrow 400 \times 9 = 3600$ and $400 \times 0·9 = 360$.

D3.5

1. 7, 14, 21, 28, 35, 42, 49, 56, 73, 70, 77, 84
2. 7, 4, 1, 8, 5, 2, 9, 6, 3, 0, 7, …
3. The 1 × and 9 × times-tables. The 1 × table unit digit sequence is the reverse of the 9 × table.
4. 1   14   142   1428   14 285   142 857   1 428 571
5.

6.

$\frac{1}{7}$	0·14285714…
$\frac{2}{7}$	0·28571428…
$\frac{3}{7}$	0·42857142…
$\frac{4}{7}$	0·57142857…
$\frac{5}{7}$	0·71428571…
$\frac{6}{7}$	0·85714285…
$\frac{7}{7}$	1

7. The digits are in the same sequence as in question 5

8.

$\frac{8}{7}$	1·14285714…
$\frac{9}{7}$	1·28571428…
$\frac{10}{7}$	1·42857142…
$\frac{11}{7}$	1·57142857…
$\frac{12}{7}$	1·71428571…
$\frac{13}{7}$	1·85714285…
$\frac{14}{7}$	2

Extra

Answers will vary.

For example: $4^3 - 7 \times 9 = 1$ and $7 \times 31 - 6^3 = 1$

$5^3 = 125$ is not close to a multiple of 7

D3.6

PCM 50

Answers will vary

E3.I

PCM 5I

1.

1	
1	1

2	
1	2

3	
1	3

4	
1	4
2	2

5	
1	5

6	
1	6
2	3

7	
1	7

8	
1	8
2	4

9	
1	9
3	3

10	
1	10
2	5

11	
1	11

12	
1	12
2	6
3	4

13	
1	13

14	
1	14
2	7

15	
1	15
3	5

2.

Record-breaker	Factors	Number of factors
1	1	1
2	1, 2	2
4	1, 2, 4	3
6	1, 2, 3, 6	4
16	1, 2, 4, 8, 16	5
12	1, 2, 3, 4, 6, 12	6
64	1, 2, 4, 8, 16, 32, 64	7
24	1, 2, 3, 4, 6, 8, 12, 24	8
36	1, 2, 3, 4, 6, 9, 12, 18, 36	9
80	1, 2, 4, 5, 8, 10, 16, 20, 40, 80	10
72	1, 2, 3, 4, 6, 8, 9, 12, 18, 24, 36, 72	12

3.

①1	2	3	④4	5	⑥6	7	8	9	10	11	⑫12
13	14	15	⑯16	17	18	19	20	21	22	23	㉔24
25	26	27	28	29	30	31	32	33	34	35	㊱36
37	38	39	40	41	42	43	44	45	46	47	48
49	50	51	52	53	54	55	56	57	58	59	60
61	62	63	⑥⑷64	65	66	67	68	69	70	71	㊲72
73	74	75	76	77	78	79	⑧⓪80	81	82	83	84
85	86	87	88	89	90	91	92	93	94	95	96
97	98	99	100	101	102	103	104	105	106	107	108
109	110	111	112	113	114	115	116	117	118	119	120

120	1, 2, 3, 4, 5, 6, 8, 10, 12, 15, 20, 24, 30, 40, 60, 120	16

E3.2

1.

9 × 12	= 108
9 × 23	= 207
9 × 34	= 306
9 × 45	= 405
9 × 56	= 504
9 × 67	= 604
9 × 78	= 702
9 × 89	= 801

2.

9 × 123	= 1107
9 × 234	= 2106
9 × 345	= 3105
9 × 456	= 4104
9 × 567	= 5103
9 × 678	= 6102
9 × 789	= 7101

3.

9 × 11	= 99
19 × 21	= 399
29 × 31	= 899
39 × 41	= 1599
49 × 51	= 2499
59 × 61	= 3599
69 × 71	= 4899
79 × 81	= 6399
89 × 91	= 8099

4.

20 × 20	= 400
19 × 21	= 399
18 × 22	= 396
17 × 23	= 391
16 × 24	= 384
15 × 25	= 375
14 × 26	= 364
13 × 27	= 351
12 × 28	= 336
11 × 29	= 319
10 × 30	= 300

5. Answers will vary.

6.

1 × 1089	= 1089
2 × 1089	= 2178
3 × 1089	= 3267
4 × 1089	= 4356
5 × 1089	= 5445
6 × 1089	= 6534
7 × 1089	= 7632
8 × 1089	= 8712
9 × 1089	= 9801
10 × 1089	= 10890

7.

1 × 9109	= 9109
2 × 9109	= 18 218
3 × 9109	= 27 327
4 × 9109	= 36 436
5 × 9109	= 45 5545
6 × 9109	= 54 654
7 × 9109	= 63 763
8 × 9109	= 72 872
9 × 9109	= 81 981
10 × 9109	= 91 090

50^2	2500
51^2	2601
52^2	2704
53^2	2809
54^2	2916
55^2	3025
56^2	3136
57^2	3249
58^2	3364
59^2	3481
60^2	3600
61^2	3721

The first two digits are consecutive numbers, but the pattern breaks down after 59^2.

E3.3

1. 92
2. 180
3. 282
4. 175
5. 456
6. 414
7. 1216
8. 215; 430; 645; 860; 1075; 1290; 1505; 1720; 1935

E3.4

1. and 2.

$1\frac{1}{2} + \frac{1}{2} + 1\frac{1}{2} + \frac{1}{2}$ $1 + 2 + 1$ $1 + 2 + 1$

$2 + 1 + 1$ $1 + 1 + 1 + 1$ $2 + 1 + 1$

  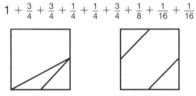

$1 + 2\frac{1}{2} + \frac{1}{2}$ $1 + \frac{3}{4} + \frac{3}{4} + \frac{1}{4} + \frac{1}{4} + \frac{3}{4} + \frac{1}{8} + \frac{1}{16} + \frac{1}{16}$

$1 + 1 + 1 + 1$ $3 + \frac{1}{2} + \frac{1}{2}$ $\frac{1}{2} + 3 + \frac{1}{2}$

$2\frac{1}{2} + \frac{1}{2} + \frac{1}{2} + \frac{1}{2}$ $\frac{1}{4} + \frac{1}{4} + 1\frac{3}{4} + 1\frac{3}{4}$ $2 + 1\frac{1}{2} + \frac{1}{2}$

$1 + 2\frac{1}{2} + \frac{1}{2}$

$\frac{1}{2} + \frac{1}{2} + 3$

$1\frac{1}{4} + \frac{3}{4} + 1\frac{3}{4} + \frac{1}{4}$

$2 + 1\frac{1}{2} + \frac{1}{2}$

E3.5

Set A: $\frac{1}{10} \rightarrow 1\cdot6 \rightarrow 2\frac{3}{4} \rightarrow 1\cdot5 \rightarrow \frac{1}{3} \rightarrow 2\cdot5$

Set B: $1\cdot5 \rightarrow \frac{5}{8} \rightarrow 2\frac{3}{4} \rightarrow 0\cdot25 \rightarrow \frac{1}{6} \rightarrow 2\cdot5$

Set C: $\frac{1}{6} \rightarrow \frac{1}{10} \rightarrow 4\cdot4 \rightarrow \frac{5}{8} \rightarrow 0\cdot25 \rightarrow 2\cdot5$

Set D: $2\frac{3}{4} \rightarrow \frac{1}{6} \rightarrow \frac{1}{3} \rightarrow 0\cdot25 \rightarrow 1\cdot6 \rightarrow 2\cdot5$

E3.6

1. 17
2. 16
3. Answers will vary.
4. Answers will vary.
5. Answers will vary.
6. Answers will vary.
7. Answers will vary.
8. 16·8
9. 77·5
10. Answers will vary.

Extra

The fraction and decimal pairs are correct.

Part of Pearson

Ginn is an imprint of Pearson Education Limited, a company incorporated in England and Wales, having its registered office at Edinburgh Gate, Harlow, Essex, CM20 2JE. Registered company number: 872828

www.pearsonschools.co.uk

Ginn is a registered trademark of Pearson Education Limited

Text © Pearson Education Limited 2009

First published 2009

13 12
10 9 8 7 6 5 4

British Library Cataloguing in Publication Data
A catalogue record for this book is available from the British Library

ISBN 978 0 602 57773 5

Typeset by Tech-Set
Cover photo/illustration © Per José Karlén
Printed in Britain by Ashford Colour Press

Acknowledgements
Every effort has been made to contact copyright holders of material reproduced in this book. Any omissions will be rectified in subsequent printings if notice is given to the publishers.

Authors

Adrian Pinel is a lecturer in mathematics and mathematics education at the University of Chichester. He has taught at both primary and secondary level, and has worked as an adviser and an educational consultant.

Jeni Pinel is an independent educational consultant and researcher, and she teaches part time at the University of Chichester. Previously, Jeni was a maths advisory teacher, and has led maths curriculum development projects in two counties.